Table of Contents

Unit 4 Earth, Moon, and Sun

Unit 5 Communities Across Time

Skills Practice

Annotated Teacher's Edition

Level 3
Book 2

Columbus, OH

SRAonline.com

Printed in the United States of America.

Send all inquiries to this address:
SRA/McGraw-Hill
4400 Easton Commons
Columbus, OH 43219-6188

ISBN: 978-0-07-610493-2
MHID: 0-07-610493-1

3 4 5 6 7 8 9 QVS 19 18 17 16 15

The McGraw-Hill Companies

Unit 6 Storytelling

Name ______________________ Date __________

Adding Suffixes *-ly* and *-y*

Focus

The suffix ***-ly*** can be added to some words.

- *-ly* often changes a word into an **adverb.** An adverb is a word that describes a verb, an adjective, or another adverb.

  light (not heavy) ⟶ **skip lightly** (skip in a light way)

- If the base word ends in *y,* change the *y* to *i* before adding *-ly.*

  happy ⟶ happily

The suffix ***-y*** can be added to some nouns.

- *-y* changes a noun into an **adjective.**

  chill (cold) ⟶ **a chilly night** (a cold night)

- Drop a final *e* before adding *-y.*

  shade ⟶ shady

- You usually double a consonant before *-y.*

  fun ⟶ funny

Practice **Read each *-ly* or *-y* word below. Write the base word on the line.**

1. cheerfully cheerful
2. noisy noise
3. deeply deep
4. richly rich

Lesson 1

Read each sentence below. Complete the definition of the underlined word.

Possible Answers

5. "I won't go!" she said loudly.

   Loudly means to do something in a loud way.

6. Pat gently picked up the puppy.

   Gently means to do something in a gentle way.

7. The children ran quickly.

   Quickly means to do something in a quick way.

8. He shook his head sadly.

   Sadly means to do something in a sad way.

Read the paragraph below. Find three mistakes the writer made when spelling *-ly* and *-y* words. Cross them out, and write the correct spellings above them.

Recently, scientists studied a ~~sanddy~~ sandy rock. They figured out that this rock used to be part of Mars. It flew quietly through space until it hit Earth. What was important, however, was that this rock had ~~curvey~~ curvy holes in it. On Earth, small living things make holes in rocks. Could there have been living things on Mars? It will take many years to discover if there ~~truely~~ truly was life on Mars.

Name ______________________ Date ____________

Adding Suffixes *-ment* and *-tion*

Focus The suffix ***-ment*** can be added to some verbs. It means "action" or "process."

- *-ment* turns a verb into a noun.

govern (to rule) → **government** (the action of ruling)

The suffix ***-tion*** can be added to some verbs. It also means "action" or "process."

- *-tion* turns a verb into a noun.

invent (to make something new) → **invention** (the action of making something new)

- Drop a final *e* before adding *-tion.* Do not double the letter *t.*

celebrate → **celebration**

Practice **Read each *-ment* or *-tion* word below. Write the base word on the line.**

1. action act
2. selection select
3. excitement excite
4. collection collect
5. agreement agree
6. argument argue

Apply **Add *-ment* to each word in the boxes below. Use the new word to complete the sentence.**

7. **treat** The doctor told Jack about a treatment for his illness.

8. **arrange** My grandmother made a flower arrangement.

9. **entertain** The concert was great entertainment.

10. **enjoy** They rode bikes in the evening for enjoyment.

Add *-tion* to each word in the boxes below. Use the new word to complete the sentence.

11. **complete** The builders worked toward the completion of the house.

12. **educate** He went to school to get a good education.

13. **relate** Tanya's uncle is her relation.

14. **celebrate** The birthday celebration included clowns and games.

Name ______________________ Date __________

Selection Vocabulary

Focus

bursts (bûrsts) *n.* plural form of **burst:** an explosion (page 23)

devices (də · vīs' · əz) *n.* plural form of **device:** a machine (page 23)

slightly (slīt' · lē) *adv.* just a little (page 26)

oval (ov' · əl) *adj.* egg-shaped (page 26)

orbit (or' · bit) *n.* the path in space that an object follows as it moves in a circle around a planet, moon, or star (page 26)

tilted (tilt' · əd) *adj.* on a slant (page 26)

horizon (hə · rī' · zən) *n.* the line where the sky and the land or sea seem to meet (page 27)

solar system (sō' · lûr · sis' · təm) *n.* the sun and all the planets, satellites, asteroids, and comets that revolve around it (page 28)

Practice

Write the vocabulary word that matches each example below.

1. an egg oval
2. the leaning Tower of Pisa tilted
3. a blender and a mixer devices
4. the moon going around Earth orbit
5. the edge of the ocean below the sky horizon
6. lava and rocks blasting from a volcano bursts

Lesson 1

Circle the vocabulary word that completes each sentence.

7. (Bursts/Horizons) of burning gas sent the Saturn V rocket into space.

8. The people in it were the last to go through the (solar system/oval) to the moon.

9. The big spacecraft stayed in (tilted/orbit) around the moon.

10. Two astronauts then flew a small, (bursts/oval) ship and landed on the moon.

11. When they landed on the moon, people on Earth knew about it (devices/slightly) less than a second later.

12. The astronauts used special (horizon/devices) to study rocks there.

13. They (slightly/tilted) and turned easily because there was less gravity.

14. The astronauts could watch Earth rise over the moon's (solar system/horizon).

Name ______________________ Date __________

Drawing Conclusions

Focus

- A reader **draws conclusions** when he or she figures out what a writer means by using information given in the story.
- A writer can give hints or details to help a reader draw conclusions.

"The year Rachel's mother started a store, she was finally able to buy Rachel a bike."

(The reader can draw the conclusion that the store made a profit.)

Practice **Read each sentence from "Sun." Answer the questions.**

Possible Answers

1. You jump out of bed, and as you wipe the sleep from your eyes, you see it.

   Conclusion: What were you doing before you jumped out of bed?

   You were sleeping.

   Clue in the text: You are wiping sleep from your eyes.

2. When the place you are on turns away from the sun, it gets dark.

   Conclusion: What time is the writer describing?

   nighttime

   Clue in the text: The text talks about a place getting dark.

Lesson 1

Read each of the following paragraphs. Write your conclusion on the line.

Possible Answers

3. After Andre finished his dinner, his grandmother handed him a box topped with a red bow. The box had holes in the top. Andre heard scratching and whining noises from inside the box.

Conclusion: Andre's grandmother gave him some kind of animal for his birthday.

4. Raven grabbed her bat and glove and opened the door. Suddenly there was a flash of light and a loud rumble. "Oh, no!" Raven groaned. "This will be the third weekend in a row."

Conclusion: Raven was going to play baseball, but it began to storm. Games have been rained out for the past three weekends.

5. Quinn walked into the school. His stomach was in knots. He did not know any of the other kids. He went to the office to find out where his classroom was.

Conclusion: Quinn is going to a new school for the first time.

Name ______________________ Date __________

Generating Ideas and Questions about Earth, the Moon, and the Sun

Answers will vary.

List things you think are interesting about Earth, the moon, the sun, or our solar system:

Sometimes I can see the moon during the day. People can travel through space. Spaceships are cool. Pluto used to be a planet, but not anymore.

What else do you want to know about the things you are interested in? Write any questions you have about Earth, the moon, the sun, and the universe here:

Why don't people move to other planets? How do you fly a spaceship? How do spaceships work? How do you become an astronaut? Why isn't Pluto a planet anymore? Is the moon made of cheese? Can we go on a field trip to the moon?

Generating Ideas and Questions about Earth, the Moon, and the Sun (continued)

The ideas and information in the unit selections can give you new ideas and questions. Answers will vary.

These are some of the most interesting ideas and facts in "Galileo's Journal 1609–1610":

The telescope used to be called a spyglass. Jupiter has four moons. Galileo made the telescope better for looking at the sky.

"Galileo's Journal 1609–1610" made me wonder these things:

Why did people think that all the stars revolved around Earth? Why were some people upset about Galileo's discoveries? How many stars are in the sky?

These are some of the most interesting ideas and facts in "Sun":

The sun is a star. The sun is the closest star to Earth. The sun is made of two gasses. The sun makes day and night on Earth.

"Sun" made me wonder these things:

How does the sun make plants grow? Does the sun make the number of days in a month? What is leap year? What is a dwarf planet?

Name ______________________ Date ___________

Explaining a Process

Think

Audience: Who will read your explanation of a process?

Possible Answer someone who wants to find out about the process

Purpose: What is your reason for explaining this process?

Possible Answer I want to help people understand how to find stars in the night sky.

Prewriting **Use this organizer as you prepare to write your explanation.**

Possible Answers

Find a good spot.

↓

Go there with a parent after dark.

↓

Let your eyes adjust for fifteen minutes.

↓

Use pointer stars to find Polaris and Little Dipper.

↓

Make up your own constellations.

Revising

Use this checklist to revise your explanation.

- ☐ Did you include all the needed steps?
- ☐ Are your words clear and specific?
- ☐ Are the sentences in the best order?
- ☐ Did you use order words such as *first* and *next?*
- ☐ Did you make your sentences different lengths so your writing sounds smooth?

Editing/Proofreading

Use this checklist to correct mistakes.

- ☐ Did you capitalize the title?
- ☐ Did you indent your paragraphs?
- ☐ Did you use correct spellings?
- ☐ Did you capitalize the first word of each sentence?
- ☐ Did you end each sentence with correct punctuation?

Publishing

Use this checklist to prepare your explanation for publication.

- ☐ Neatly rewrite or type a final copy.
- ☐ Add a drawing to show each step of your process.

UNIT 4 Lesson 1

Name ______________________ Date __________

Spelling

Focus The suffix ***-ly*** can be added to some words. *-ly* changes the word into an **adverb,** which is a word that describes a verb, an adjective, or another adverb. If the base word ends in *y*, change the *y* to *i* before adding *-ly*.

The suffix ***-y*** can be added to some nouns. *-y* changes a noun into an **adjective.** Drop a final *e* before adding *-y*. You usually double a consonant before *-y*.

The suffixes ***-ment*** and ***-tion*** mean "action or process."

When adding the suffix *-tion*, if the base word ends in *t*, drop the *t* and add *-tion*.

Word List

1. slightly
2. kindly
3. partly
4. daily
5. scary
6. chewy
7. rusty
8. bony
9. shipment
10. payment
11. treatment
12. statement
13. selection
14. invention
15. action

Challenge Words

16. apartment
17. easily

Practice **Sort the spelling words under the correct heading.**

Order will vary under heading.

Changed *y* to *i*, add *-ly*

1. daily

Suffix *-ly*

2. kindly
3. partly
4. slightly

Spelling (continued)

Suffix *-y*

5. chewy
6. rusty

Dropped final *e*, added *-y*

7. scary
8. bony

Suffix *-ment*

9. shipment
10. payment
11. treatment
12. statement

Suffix *-tion*

13. selection
14. invention
15. action

Name ______________________ Date __________

Commas

Focus

- Use commas to separate items in a list of three or more things. This list is also called a **series.**

Examples: The deer ate our **lettuce, cabbage,** and **carrots.**

Bees, flies, and **ants** are insects.

- Use a comma after *yes* and *no* at the beginning of a sentence.

Examples: No, we are out of bananas.

Yes, they did leave.

Practice **If the use of commas is correct, write *yes.* If commas are used incorrectly, write *no.***

1. The Ortegas traveled through Illinois, Minnesota South Dakota, and Wyoming. no

2. No, they did not go to Montana. yes

3. They packed snacks, games, and bottles of water. yes

4. They saw the Badlands, Mount Rushmore, and Yellowstone. yes

5. Yes they had a wonderful time. no

Insert commas where they are needed in each passage below.

6. Stargazing is a great way to spend an evening. To get the best view, get away from the city lights. When going stargazing, find a good spot to see stars,bring good binoculars,and wait until it is dark. Bring food, water,a constellation chart,and a special red flashlight. The red flashlight will be dim enough that you can still see stars. Use it with the constellation chart to help you find the star pictures. On a clear night, you may see Orion, the Pleiades,the Big Dipper,and the North Star. Stargazing can be a lot of fun.

7. Dear Beth,

My trip from Chicago to Yellowstone National Park has been fun. Yes,there were lots of animals. No,I didn't get to see any bears.

We camped in the Badlands. Yes,the air was clearer, and I saw so many stars. My dad stayed up with me. We used his telescope and found Venus,Mars,and Saturn. He showed me craters, peaks,and valleys on the moon.

We'll be back soon. I've been taking lots of pictures, so you'll be able to see everything.

Your friend,

Cindy Ortega

Name ______________________ Date __________

Outlining

Focus

An **outline** is a way of organizing information. You can outline the important points in a book or in an article.

- The most important points are usually written after Roman numerals (I, II, III, IV).

  I. The Solar System

- The secondary points are usually written after capital letters (A, B, C, D).

  A. The sun

- The next lowest points are usually written after numbers (1, 2, 3, 4).

  1. The sun is a star.

  2. The sun is hot.

Practice

Arrange the list below of "Things to Do on Saturday" and put them in the outline below.

Possible Answer

Do homework
Eat lunch
Morning
Eat dinner
Read
Evening
Eat breakfast
Afternoon
Ride bike

I. Morning
  A. Eat breakfast
  B. Ride bike
II. Afternoon
  A. Eat lunch
  B. Do homework
III. Evening
  A. Eat dinner
  B. Read

Outlining (continued)

Read the outline below. It outlines the information from pages 21, 22, and 23 in "Sun." Reread those pages of the story to fill in the missing parts of the outline.

Possible Answers

I. What is the sun like?

A. Not made of rock

B. Made of two gases

1. Hydrogen
2. Helium

C. Its surface

1. Gas explosions
2. 11,000 °C

II. Studying the sun

A. Sun safety

1. Never look right at it.
2. Even sunglasses can't keep you safe.

B. How scientists study it

1. They use special telescope filters.
2. They use cameras.

Name ______________________ Date __________

Suffixes *-ful* and *-able*

Focus

The suffix ***-ful*** can be added to some nouns. This suffix means "full of."

- *-ful* changes the word into an adjective.

  sorrow ("sadness") → **sorrowful** ("full of sadness")

- If the base word ends in *y*, change the *y* to *i* before adding *-ful.*

  beauty → **beautiful**

The suffix ***-able*** can be added to verbs or nouns. This suffix means "able or tending to be" something.

- *-able* changes the word into an adjective.

  read ("to understand printed words") → **readable** ("able to be read")

- For most base words ending in *e*, drop the *e* before adding *-able.*

  adore → **adorable**

Practice

Read each *-ful* and *-able* word below. Write the base word on the line.

1. likable ______like______
2. joyful ______joy______
3. dutiful ______duty______
4. fixable ______fix______
5. mistakable ______mistake______

Lesson 2

Read each sentence. Correctly add *-ful* to each base word in the box to complete the sentence.

6. **use** Hans Lippershey made the first useful telescope.

7. **care** Galileo first used it to make a careful study of the sky.

8. **power** Galileo found powerful proof that the sun did not orbit Earth.

9. **harm** Many people thought Galileo's ideas were harmful.

10. **law** They were not lawful at the time.

Read each sentence. Correctly add *-able* to each base word in the box to complete the sentence.

11. **view** A telescope takes in viewable light from faraway objects.

12. **use** It uses the light to make a usable picture.

13. **gather** The bigger the lens, the more light is gatherable.

14. **desire** For scientists, a large telescope is desirable.

15. **accept** For most people, a simple one is acceptable.

Name ____________________ Date __________

Inflectional Endings *-ed* and *-ing*

Remember, when the **inflectional endings** *-ed* and *-ing* are added to a base word, the tense of the base word changes.

- The ***-ed*** ending shows an action that happened in the past.

  play + ed = played The children played yesterday.

- The ***-ing*** ending shows an action that is happening now.

  play + ing = playing The children are playing now.

- If a word ends in *consonant -y,* change the *y* to an *i* before adding *-ed.* **study studied**
- For some words ending in *consonant-vowel-consonant,* double the final letter before adding *-ed* or *-ing.*

  tap tapping

Read the sentence from page 39 of "Grandmother Spider Brings the Sun." Answer the questions below.

Wolf gathered all the animals together in a big cave.

1. Circle *gather,* meaning "to collect," in the word below:

gathered

2. Knowing how the ending *-ed* changes the meaning of a word, what does the word *gathered* mean? to collect in the past

3. How would you add *-ing* to *gather?* gathering

Apply **Read the sentences from pages 40 and 43 of "Grandmother Spider Brings the Sun." Answer the questions below.**

Possible Answers

The other animals nodded in agreement.

4. The base word *nod* means "to move your head up and down." What does the word *nodding* mean?

to move your head up and down now

5. How did the spelling of *nod* change when *-ed* was added?

The writer doubled the final letter before adding -ed.

6. Add *-ing* to *nod,* and use the word in a sentence of your own.

The girl is nodding because she wants to go.

Possum struggled over to the sun, took a little piece, and put it inside his big ol' bushy tail.

7. The base word *struggle* means "to make a great effort." What does the word *struggled* mean?

to make a great effort in the past

8. How did the spelling of *struggle* change when *-ed* was added?

The writer dropped the e.

9. Add *-ing* to *struggle,* and use the word in a sentence of your own.

I am struggling to climb the tall hill.

Name ______________________ Date __________

Selection Vocabulary

Focus

directions (də • rek' • shənz) *n.* plural form of **direction:** the way to get somewhere (page 38)

sneak (snēk) *v.* to go quietly without being seen (page 40)

bushy (bo͝osh' • ē) *adj.* shaggy and thick (page 42)

squinty (skwint' • ē) *adj.* eyes partly closed (page 43)

ringed (ringd) *adj.* marked with a circular pattern (page 43)

clay (klā) *n.* soft, sticky mud (page 49)

tight (tīt) *adj.* fitting very closely together (page 50)

rays (rāz) *n.* plural form of **ray:** a beam of light or energy (page 51)

Practice A **Circle the vocabulary word that describes the underlined words in each sentence below.**

1. The children walk very quietly past the sleeping baby.
   tight (sneak)
2. The tree had bulky leaves.
   (bushy) clay
3. Light beams shone over the horizon.
   (rays) squinty
4. The potter made a cup out of soft mud.
   (clay) tight
5. Her eyes were almost closed because of the bright light.
   busy (squinty)

Apply **Write a vocabulary word to complete each sentence below.**

6. In a Native American story, a bear with thick, bushy fur saw seven girls.

7. They tried to sneak away, but the bear chased them.

8. The girls did not have directions for getting away.

9. They stood close and tight on a rock.

10. Suddenly the rock grew tall, and the bear stared with squinty eyes.

11. He scraped the clay on the rock, but he could not climb up.

12. This tells why Devil's Tower is ringed with deep marks.

13. The girls became stars whose rays light up the night sky.

Name ______________________ Date __________

Author's Purpose

Focus The **author's purpose** is the main reason he or she is telling a story in a certain way.

- The purpose can be to *inform,* to *explain,* to *entertain,* or to *persuade.*
- An author can have more than one purpose for writing.
- The purpose affects the way details, descriptions, story events, and dialogue are created.

Practice **Read each group of sentences below. Then, write the author's purpose for writing.**

1. First, I mixed the two colors of paint in a large bucket and stirred carefully. Then, I washed the kitchen wall. After the wall was dry, I began to paint it.

Author's Purpose: to explain or to inform

2. I hope you will agree with me that the park on Green Street should be kept open until 8:00 P.M. during the summer. This would help everyone who lives in our neighborhood. Many people can only use the park after work.

Author's Purpose: to persuade

Reread "Grandmother Spider Brings the Sun." Answer the questions below.

Possible Answers

3. Look through the story. Find one of the author's purposes. to explain

4. What is one story event that shows this purpose? The author tells why the buzzard is bald.

5. What is another possible purpose? to entertain

6. What is one story event that shows this purpose? The author tells about how sneaky Grandmother Spider is.

7. Write a short paragraph that informs the reader of something.
The moon shines because it reflects the sun's light. It seems to change shape during the month. At certain times, we cannot see it at all.

Name ______________________ Date __________

Choosing an Investigation Question

What is a good investigation question?

Your group investigation question can be about anything related to the unit. A good investigation question will **not** have a "yes" or "no" answer. A good investigation question will require a lot of **thinking** and **research.**

Read the following questions and decide whether the question is a good investigation question. Then explain why or why not.

Answers will vary.

Question 1: Can you drive a car on the moon?
Is this a good investigation question? No

Why or why not? The answer is either "yes" or "no."

Question 2: Will Earth ever stop spinning?
Is this a good investigation question? No

Why or why not? The answer is either "yes" or "no."

Question 3: Why is Earth round instead of some other shape?
Is this a good investigation question? Yes

Why or why not? Because to answer this, you have to do a lot of research.

Question 4: What makes a good friend?
Is this a good investigation question? No

Why or why not? The question is not about the unit.

Choosing an Investigation Question (continued)

Some initial questions might not be very good investigation questions, but they can be revised. **Take the questions from previous page that were not good investigation questions and revise them to make them better.** Hint: change "yes" or "no" questions and questions about facts to questions beginning with *how* or *why*.

Example: Can you drive a car on the moon?
This question is not a good investigation question because it has a "yes" or "no" answer. By revising this question, it can become a good investigation question.

Revision: How could you make a car that could drive on the moon?
This is a good question because you would need to research a lot about both the moon and cars.

Revised questions from the previous page: **Answers will vary.**

Why does Earth spin? How does Earth spin?

What would happen if Earth stopped spinning?

Name ______________________ Date __________

Writing a Trickster Tale

Think

Audience: Who will read your trickster tale?

Possible Answer my friends

Purpose: What is your purpose for writing the tale?

Possible Answer I want to tell a story about why cats can see when it's dark.

Prewriting

Use this organizer as you prepare to write your trickster tale. Write the main events for your story's beginning, middle, and end.

Possible Answers

Possible Title The Cat's Eyes

Beginning
The cat wants to see in the dark.

↓

Middle
The cat races the moon and wins its light.

↓

End
The cat puts the moon's light in its eyes.

Revising

Use this checklist to revise your trickster tale.

- ☐ Does your story have a clear beginning, middle, and end?
- ☐ Do the personalities of each character come through?
- ☐ Does the story build to a climax?
- ☐ Does the story have a conclusion?

Editing/Proofreading

Use this checklist to correct mistakes.

- ☐ Did you capitalize your title?
- ☐ Did you indent your paragraphs?
- ☐ Did you use correct spellings?
- ☐ Did you use describing words?
- ☐ Did you use action words?

Publishing

Use this checklist to prepare your trickster tale for publication.

- ☐ Neatly rewrite or type a final copy.
- ☐ Add a drawing of the trickster in your tale.

Name ______________________ Date __________

Spelling

Focus

The suffix ***-ful*** means "full of." The suffix ***-able*** means "able or tending to be."

Remember, the inflectional ending ***-ed*** shows an action that happened in the past.

The inflectional ending ***-ing*** shows an action that is happening now.

When adding suffixes or inflectional endings, for words ending in:

- silent *e*, drop the e before adding the ending.
- consonant *-y*, change the *y* to *i* before adding the ending.
- *consonant-vowel-consonant*, double the final letter before adding *-ed* and *-ing*.

Word List

1. ringed
2. painful
3. fixable
4. scared
5. helpful
6. filling
7. pleasing
8. wishful
9. notable
10. stunning
11. wearable
12. dressing
13. clogged
14. harmful
15. likable

Challenge Words

16. wonderful
17. injured

Practice

Sort the spelling words under the correct heading.
Order will vary under heading.

Suffix *-ful*

1. painful
2. helpful
3. wishful
4. harmful

Spelling (continued)

Dropped *e*, added *-able*

5. likable

6. notable

Suffix *-able*

7. fixable

8. wearable

Dropped *e*, added inflectional ending *-ing*

9. pleasing

Doubled the consonant, added inflectional ending *-ing* and *-ed*

10. stunning

11. clogged

Added inflectional ending *-ing*

12. filling

13. dressing

Dropped *e*, added inflectional ending *-ed*

14. scared

Inflectional ending *-ed*

15. ringed

Name ______________________ Date __________

Compound Words and Contractions

Remember, compound words and contractions are both ways of joining two words.

- A **compound word** can have the same meaning as the two words in it, or it can have a new meaning.

  basketball = "the ball that is used to play basketball"
  (not "a basket that is a ball")

- When you make a **contraction,** you take out one or more letters. An apostrophe shows where a missing letter or letters were.

  I am = I'm

  Many contractions use the words *is, are,* and *will.*

  Many contractions have the word *not* in them with an apostrophe in place of the *o.*

  do not = don't

Underline the contractions in the following paragraph. Circle any compound words.

Rosa Parks boarded a bus in Montgomery, Alabama, on December 1, 1955. When she sat at the front of the bus, the bus driver did not give her a handshake. He said, "Don't sit in that seat. You're not allowed." Parks replied, "I'm tired from a long day of work, and it's a seat just like any other seat. I shouldn't have to sit in the back just because of the color of my skin." Newspapers printed stories about Parks's action. Her bravery made headlines.

Lesson 2

Use a compound word from the box to fill in each blank below.

birthday	scarecrow	skateboard	birdhouse

1. The scarecrow in the field kept animals away.

2. You need a special birdhouse for purple martins.

3. The girl brought a special snack to celebrate her birthday.

4. Evan rides his skateboard to school.

Fill in each blank with the contraction made from the boldfaced words.

It is It's early morning, but Akili and I **are not** aren't asleep. **We are** We're in the kitchen, and we **do not** don't want to make any noise. **We are** We're cooking a surprise breakfast for our parents.

"I **cannot** can't reach the pan to cook the eggs," Akili whispered. "**It is** It's on top of the refrigerator."

Lesson 2

Name ______________________ Date __________

Following Directions

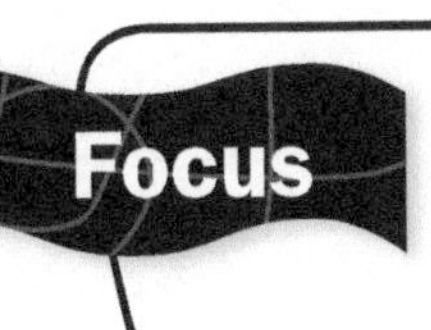

Directions let you know how to do something. If you are **following directions,** you follow the order of what the directions tell you to do.

Read the following set of directions. Answer the questions below.

How to Photograph Stars

1. To gather the light of stars, you must take a picture over a long period of time. First, find a clear, dark spot.
2. Next, set up your camera on a tripod.
3. Open the shutter. This allows the camera to continue gathering light.
4. Wait several hours.
5. Close the shutter.
6. Develop the film. You will see the stars' "tracks."

1. What are these directions telling about?
   how to photograph stars
2. What would you need to follow these directions?
   a camera, a tripod, a dark spot, film

Follow the directions below.

3. Color the land brown.

4. Color the water around the land blue.

5. Draw an *X* over North America.

6. Draw a large circle around Earth.

7. Draw a grey dot on the circle.

8. Write *the moon* next to the dot.

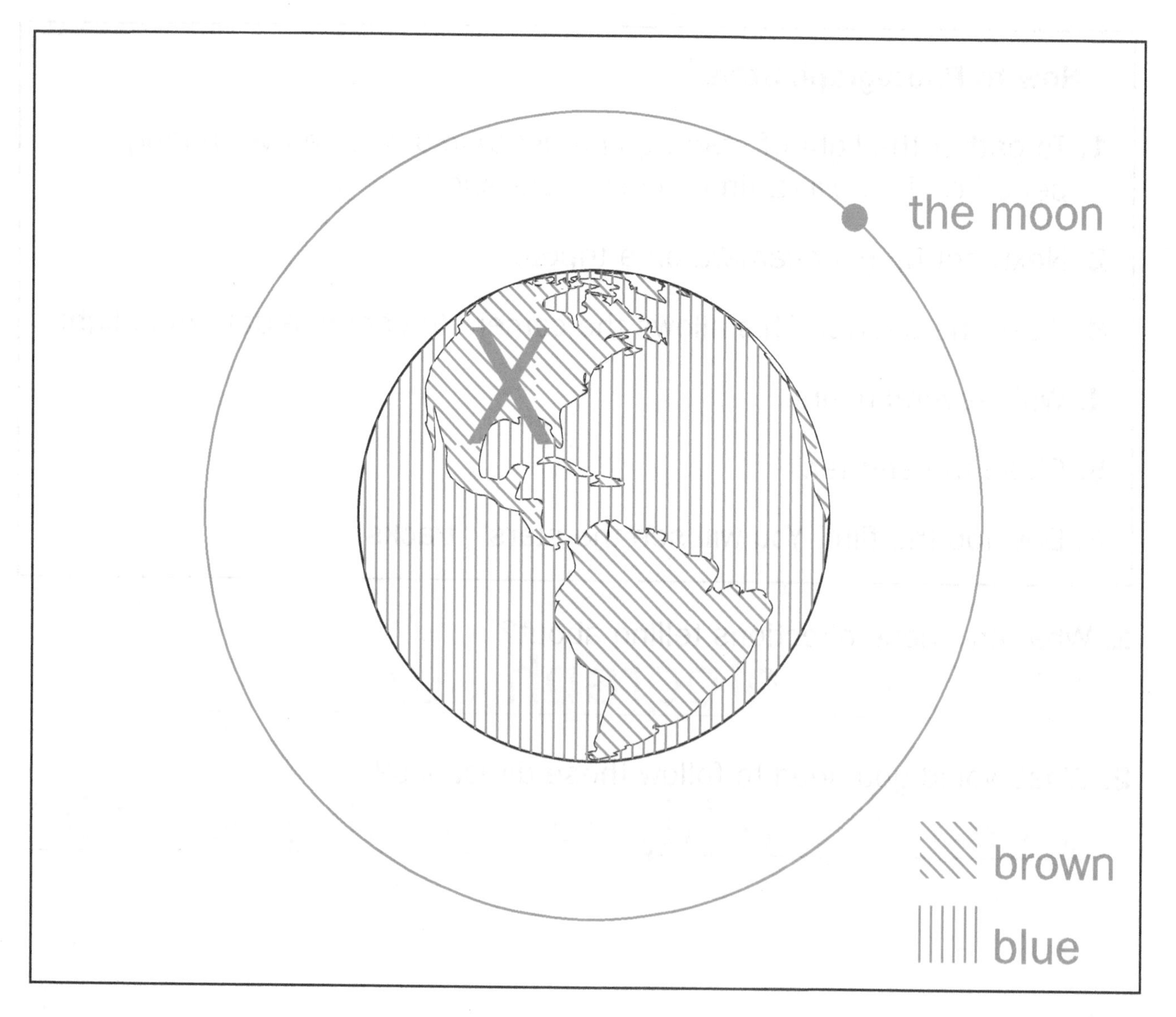

UNIT 4 **Lesson 3**

Name ______________________ Date __________

Suffixes *-ity* and *-less*

Focus

The suffix ***-ity*** can be added to some adjectives. The suffix means "state of being."

- *-ity* changes the word into a noun.

  real ("something that is") ⟶ **reality** ("the state of being real")

- If the base word ends in *e,* drop the *e* before adding *-ity.*

  rare ⟶ **rarity**

The suffix ***-less*** can be added to some nouns. The suffix means "without" or "not having."

- *-less* changes a noun into an adjective.

  worth ("having value") ⟶ **worthless** ("without value")

Practice **Correctly add *-ity* to each word below.**

1. electric electricity

2. rare rarity

3. popular popularity

Correctly add *-less* to each word below.

4. end endless

5. use useless

6. power powerless

Lesson 3

Use the words you made on the previous page to complete the sentences below. The definition of each missing word is shown in parentheses.

7. We are powerless to make more oil, so we must find energy in new places. (without power)
8. The sun's energy is not useless. (without use)
9. Solar panels change it into electricity. (a special form of energy)
10. Years ago, these panels were a rarity. (the state of being rare)
11. Now they are gaining in popularity. (the state of being popular)
12. The good thing is that the sun's energy is almost endless. (without end)

Write a word ending in *-less* that means the opposite of each word below.

13. hopeful hopeless
14. restful restless
15. thoughtful thoughtless
16. joyful joyless

Name ______________________________ Date ____________

Suffixes *-ness* and *-sion*

The suffix ***-ness*** can be added to some adjectives. The suffix means "state of being."

- *-ness* changes the word into a noun.

  kind ("gentle") ⟶ **kindness** ("the state of being gentle")

- If the base word ends in *y*, change the *y* to *i* before adding *-ness.* **happy** ⟶ **happiness**

The suffix ***-sion*** can be added to some verbs. The suffix means "the action of" something.

- *-sion* is another form of the suffix *-tion.* It changes words into nouns.

  collide ("to hit") ⟶ **collision** ("the action of things hitting")

- *-sion* is used when verbs end in *de* or *se.* Drop *de* or *se* before adding *-sion.*

  revise ⟶ **revision** **decide** ⟶ **decision**

Add the given suffix to each word below. Write the new word and the meaning of the new word on the lines.

Word	Suffix	New Word	New Meaning
1. sweet	-ness	the state of being sweet	sweetness
2. divide	-sion	the action of dividing	division
3. confuse	-sion	the action of confusing	confusion
4. good	-ness	the state of being good	goodness
5. empty	-ness	the state of being empty	emptiness

Lesson 3

Write sentences using two of the words you made in the Practice section. Possible Answers

6. I used division to divide the number.

7. The boy didn't like the candy's sweetness.

Think about each word's meaning. Circle the word that correctly completes each sentence below.

8. She was full of ______________ and wanted to cry.
   a. sadness **b.** decision

9. Glasses can help your ______________.
   a. awkwardness **b.** vision

10. The rocket's ______________ was very loud.
   a. brightness **b.** explosion

11. The teachers had a ______________ about the school's rules.
   a. closeness **b.** discussion

Name ______________________________ Date __________

Selection Vocabulary

Focus

quarter moon (kwor' · tər mo͞on') *n.* phase of the moon in which it looks like a half circle (page 62)

sliver (sliv' · ûr) *n.* a thin, narrow piece (page 62)

crescent moon (kres' · ənt mo͞on') *n.* the curved shape of the waxing or waning moon (page 62)

new moon (no͞o mo͞on') *n.* the moon when it cannot be seen or when it appears as a thin crescent (page 65)

occur (ək · kûr') *v.* to happen (page 68)

phases (fāz' · əz) *n.* plural form of **phase:** the appearance and shape of the moon or a planet as it is seen at a particular time (page 68)

Practice **Look at the diagram below. Write the missing words next to the correct pictures. Write the missing vocabulary word from the diagram's title.**

Some Phases **of the Moon**

full moon

quarter moon

crescent moon

Read each fact below. Rewrite the fact using a vocabulary word.

Possible Answers

1. The moon goes through many shapes during a month.
   The moon goes through many phases in a month.
2. These changes happen because the moon orbits Earth.
   These changes occur because the moon orbits Earth.
3. Sometimes the moon looks like a small, thin thing.
   Sometimes the moon looks like a sliver.
4. Other times you can see one-half of the moon.
   Other times you can see a quarter moon.
5. There are times when you cannot see the moon at all.
   There are times when there is a new moon.
6. As the moon seems to grow or shrink, you can see the curved shape of the waxing or waning moon.
   As the moon seems to grow or shrink, you can see a crescent moon.

Name ____________________ Date __________

Compare and Contrast

Writers sometimes compare and contrast in a story to make an idea clearer and to make the story more interesting for the reader.

- To **compare** means to tell how things, events, or characters are alike.
- To **contrast** means to tell how things, events, or characters are different.

Read each sentence. Underline the two things that are being compared. Then, answer the questions.

Possible Answers

1. A <u>bird</u> is like an <u>airplane</u>.

How are they alike? They both have wings. They both can fly.

How are they different? A bird is a living creature. An airplane is a machine.

2. A <u>dog</u> is like a <u>cat</u>.

How are they alike? They each have four legs, are covered with fur, and make good pets.

How are they different? They are different kinds of animals.

Lesson 3

Read the sentence from "The Moon Seems to Change." Answer the questions below.

While one half of Earth is having sunshine and daylight, the other half is getting no sunshine.

3. Does the sentence above compare things or contrast things?

contrast

4. What two things are being compared or contrasted?

The day side of Earth is being contrasted with the night side of Earth.

5. Explain how these two things are both alike and different.

Alike: they are both sides of Earth. Different: one is dark and not facing the sun, while the other is light and facing the sun.

Write a sentence comparing the shape of the full moon with something else. Make sure to explain how they are alike.

Possible Answer The shape of the full moon is like an orange, because they are both round and shaped like a circle.

Name ______________________ Date __________

Identifying Investigation Needs and Making Plans

Use this page to help make a plan for your group investigation. **Answers will vary.**

These are things we already know about our topic:

Earth spins on its axis. Earth orbits around the sun.

Finding more information will help you confirm or revise your conjectures. These are things we still need to do or find out:

How fast does Earth spin? What causes Earth to spin? What started Earth spinning? Have Earth and the other planets always spun? Do the other planets spin as fast as Earth?

These are people who might be experts about our topic:

an astronaut, an astronomer, a science teacher

Identifying Investigation Needs and Making Plans (continued)

In your groups, for each source below, check whether you think it would be useful or not useful. Answers will vary.

Possible Sources	Useful	Not useful
Encyclopedias	✔	
Books		✔
Magazines		✔
Newspapers		✔
Films or TV shows		✔
Interviews	✔	
Personal observation		✔
Museums	✔	
Internet sites		✔
Other Materials		

For each source that you checked as useful above, write down specific titles, people, or places you could use as a source. Then, write how each will be useful. Possible Answers

Title or Name of Source: Encyclopedia

How this source will be useful: An encyclopedia will tell how fast Earth spins.

Title or Name of Source: Museums

How this source will be useful: Space museums have objects to see about spacecraft and Earth.

Title or Name of Source: Interview

How this source will be useful: Space scientists have been to space or study a lot about space and would know about Earth and why it spins the way it does.

Name ______________________ Date __________

Writing Directions

Audience: Who will read your directions?

Possible Answer a friend who will come to my house

Purpose: What is your purpose for writing the directions?

Possible Answer I want my friend to be able to visit me.

Use this organizer to help you plan your directions. Write each step in order. Add more boxes if needed.

Possible Answers

From the school, turn left on Main Street.

↓

Walk 2 blocks.

↓

Turn right on Idyllwild Ave.

↓

Walk 1 block.

↓

My house is blue. The address is 153 Idyllwild Ave.

Revising

Use this checklist to revise your directions.

- ☐ Did you include all needed steps?
- ☐ Are the sentences in the best order?
- ☐ Did you number sentences to help your reader?
- ☐ Are your words clear and specific?

Editing/Proofreading

Use this checklist to correct mistakes.

- ☐ Did you number your sentences correctly?
- ☐ Did you use correct spellings?
- ☐ Did you use correct direction words?
- ☐ Did you explain where the directions begin and end?

Publishing

Use this checklist to prepare your directions for publication.

- ☐ Neatly rewrite or type a final copy.
- ☐ Draw a map to help illustrate your directions.

Name ______________________ Date __________

Spelling

Focus The suffixes ***-ity*** and ***-ness*** mean "state of being."

The suffix ***-less*** means "without."

The suffix ***-sion*** means "the action of" something.

When adding the suffixes *-ity* or *-sion* to words with a silent *e,* drop the *e* before adding the suffix. For base words ending in *de* or *se* drop *de* or *se* before adding the suffix *-sion. decide, decision*

Word List

1. weakness
2. tension
3. sleepless
4. rarity
5. endless
6. sanity
7. fitness
8. priceless
9. purity
10. erosion
11. blindness
12. electricity
13. fairness
14. division
15. careless

Challenge Words

16. breathless
17. explosion

Practice **Sort the spelling words under the correct heading.**

Order will vary under heading.

Dropped e, added suffix *-ity*

1. rarity
2. sanity
3. purity

Suffix *-ity*

4. electricity

Suffix *-less*

5. sleepless
6. endless

Spelling (continued)

7. priceless

8. careless

Suffix *-ness*

9. weakness

10. fitness

11. blindness

12. fairness

Dropped *se,* added suffix *-sion*

13. tension

Dropped *de,* added suffix *-sion*

14. erosion

15. division

Name ______________________ Date __________

Adverbs

Focus

Remember that an **adverb** tells more about a verb, an adjective, or another adverb.

She ran quickly. (*quickly* tells about the verb *ran*)

You're speaking too quietly. (*too* tells about the adverb *quietly*)

- Many adverbs are words that end in *-ly.*

slowly, happily, gently

- When describing a good action, make sure to use the adverb *well.*

Incorrect: **She draws good.** Correct: **She draws well.**

Practice **Match each adverb with its correct category below.**

1. lately
2. slowly
3. certainly
4. everywhere

a. tells how certain we are about something that happens
b. tells how something is done
c. tells where something happens
d. tells when something happens

Lesson 3

Write an adverb that is the opposite of each underlined word below.

5. The moon does not orbit Earth quickly. It orbits Earth slowly.

6. The rocket travels forward. It does not travel backward.

7. The puppy sees badly. It does not see well.

8. I never watch sports. I always watch movies instead.

9. Meteorites fall down to Earth. They do not go up.

Read each of the following compound sentences. Finish the sentence, and make sure to use an adverb.

Possible Answers

10. The girl had to say no, so she shook her head sadly.

11. I like to pack my lunch, and I often eat peanut butter and jelly

12. The cat jumped up, and it quickly ran away.

Name ______________________ Date ____________

Diagrams

Focus A **diagram** is a special kind of plan, drawing, or outline.

- It can show how something works.
- It can label or explain parts of something.
- It can show the relationship between parts of something.

Practice **Use the diagram to answer the questions below.**

The Sun

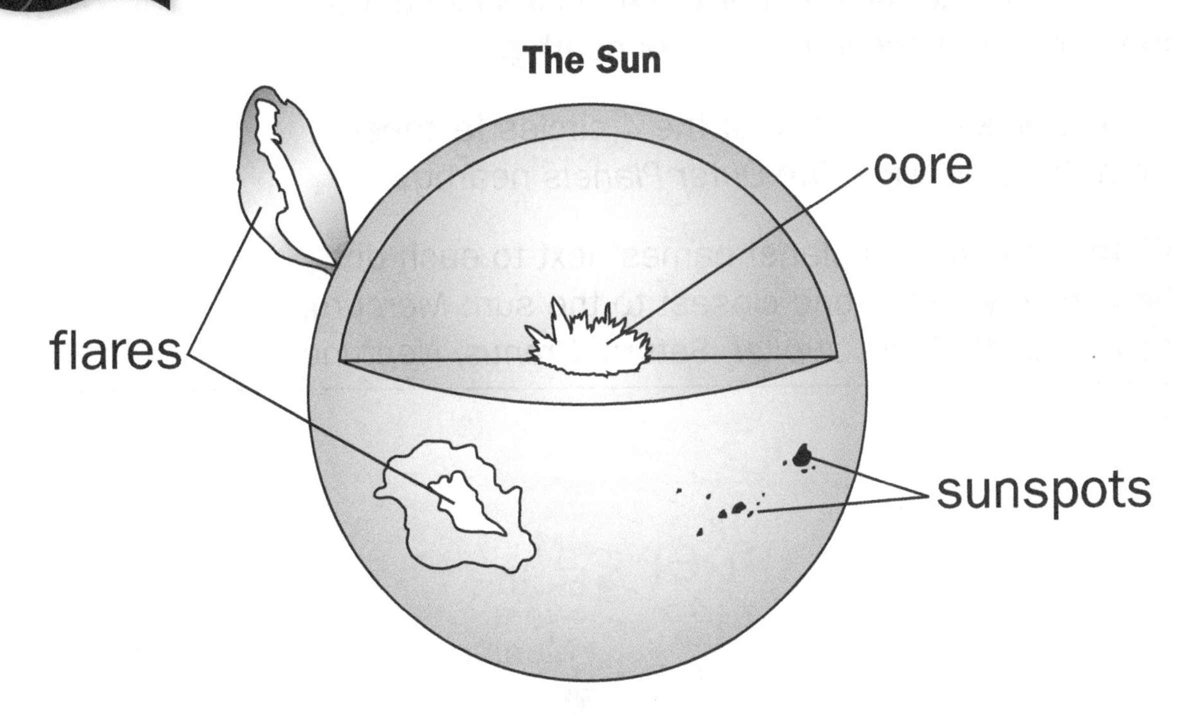

1. What is the area in the middle of the sun? the core
2. What are the black dots on the sun? sunspots
3. What part of the sun looks like leaping fire? flare

Diagrams (continued)

Follow the directions to make your own diagram of the solar system. Use another sheet of paper if necessary.

The Solar System

1. Draw a yellow dot in the middle of the box. This shows the sun.
2. Draw 8 black circles around the sun. These will show the path each planet travels. As they get farther away from the sun, make the circles bigger.
3. Draw a blue dot on each of the 4 circles closest to the sun. Write *The Inner Planets* nearby.
4. Draw a pink dot on each of the 4 circles farthest from the sun. Write *The Outer Planets* nearby.
5. Write the following planet names next to each dot, beginning with the one closest to the sun: *Mercury, Venus, Earth, Mars, Jupiter, Saturn, Uranus, Neptune.*

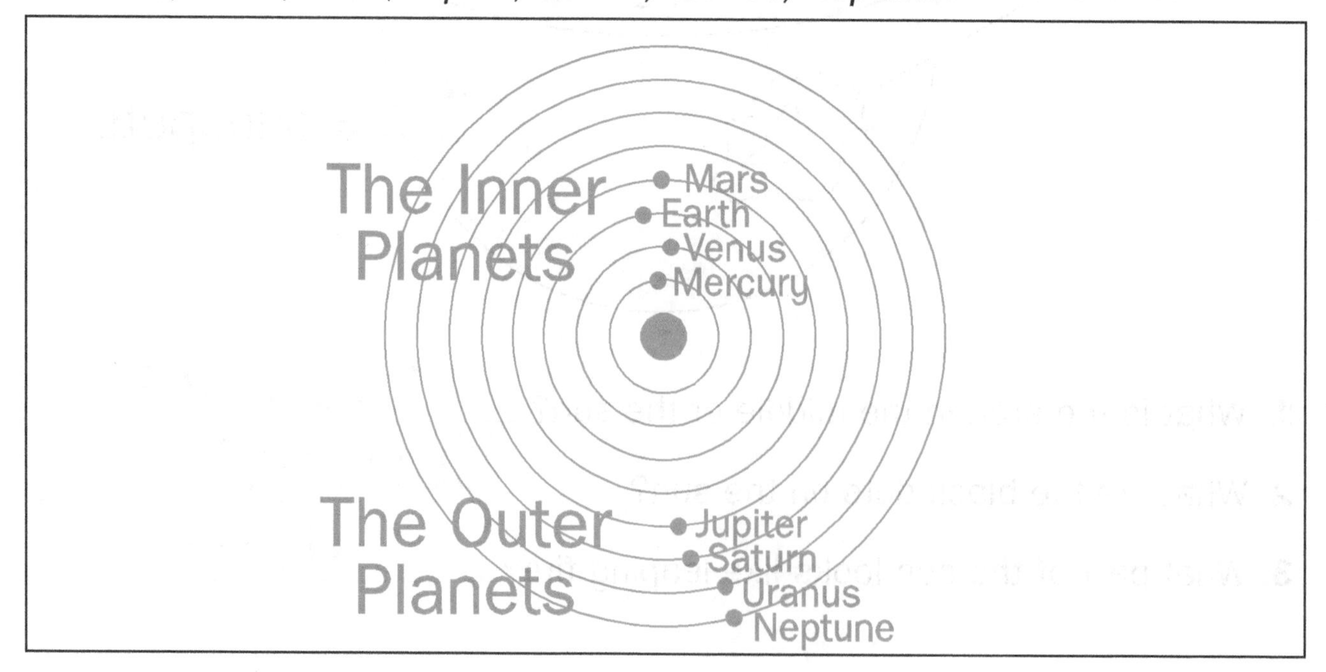

Name ______________________ Date __________

Greek Root Words *ast, graph, log,* and *scop*

Focus

Greek roots are word parts that have certain meanings. Knowing about a root in a new word can help you understand its meaning.

- The root ***ast*** means "star." It is used in words such as *astronaut.*
- The root ***graph*** means "something written or drawn." It is used in words such as *autograph.*
- The root ***log*** (sometimes spelled *logue*) means "to speak." It is used in words such as *dialogue.*
- The root ***scop*** means "to look at or examine." It is used in words such as *telescope.*

Practice

Look for the Greek root inside each word below. Connect each word with its meaning.

1. asteroid
2. microscope
3. autograph
4. monologue
5. asterisk

a. a tool used to look at small things
b. a star-shaped symbol
c. a small rock orbiting a star
d. a person's handwritten name
e. a speech in a play that is spoken by one person

Apply **Circle the word in each sentence that contains a Greek root. Use context clues to figure out the word's meaning. Circle the correct definition.**

6. The astronomer spent a lot of time watching stars in the night sky.
   a. a person who studies writing
   b. a person who studies stars
7. Madeline bought a new camera for her photography class.
   a. the process of making pictures with a camera
   b. the study of making speeches
8. The actor gave a prologue before the play.
   a. a speech given by an actor at the beginning of a play
   b. a person who examines plays
9. When I looked through the telescope, I could see Saturn's rings.
   a. a tool that makes faraway things seem close
   b. a tool that helps you write
10. The astronaut floated in space near the space shuttle.
   a. a person who writes about space
   b. a person who travels into space
11. People used to send written messages over telegraph wires.
   a. a machine that sends spoken messages over long distances
   b. a machine that sends written messages over long distances

Name ______________________ Date __________

Latin Root Words *grat, mar, miss,* and *port*

Latin roots are word parts that have certain meanings. Knowing about a root in a new word can help you understand its meaning.

- The root ***grat*** means "thankful or pleasing." It is used in words such as *grateful.*
- The root ***mar*** means "sea or ocean." It is used in words such as *marine.*
- The root ***miss*** (sometimes spelled *mit*) means "sent." It is used in words such as *mission.*
- The root ***port*** means "carry." It is used in words such as *portable.*

Read each word and its meaning below. Circle the Latin root inside it. Write the root's meaning.

1. congratulated ("to have told people you are happy for them")
thankful or pleasing

2. transport ("to move something from one place to another")
carry

3. mission ("a special job a person is sent to finish")
sent

4. marine ("relating to the sea") sea or ocean

5. support ("to help") carry

Lesson 4

Use each word from the previous page to complete a sentence below.

6. In 1998, a spacecraft was sent to ___transport___ cameras and other machines to Mars.
7. The spacecraft's ___mission___ was to find out about the history of water on Mars.
8. If Mars once had water, then it might have had ___marine___ bacteria. These are small things that live in water.
9. People back on Earth worked to ___support___ and guide the spacecraft.
10. Other scientists ___congratulated___ these people for their good work.

Use four of the words from the previous page in sentences of your own. **Possible Answers**

11. A police officer's mission is to protect people.
12. A whale is a marine animal.
13. Trucks transport food to stores.
14. The beams support the bridge.

Lesson 4

Name ______________________ Date __________

Selection Vocabulary

Focus

astronaut (as' • tro • not') *n.* a person who is trained to pilot or be a part of the crew of a spacecraft (page 80)

commander (kəm • mand' • ûr) *n.* the captain leading a ship or voyage (page 80)

gigantic (jī • gan' • tik) *adj.* very big (page 82)

orbit (or' • bit) *v.* to circle around a heavenly body, such as Earth or the moon (page 82)

gravity (gra' • və • tē) *n.* the force pulling things toward the center of a body in space, such as Earth or the moon (page 84)

pressure (presh' • ûr) *n.* weight of one thing pushing against another (page 84)

Practice **Use a vocabulary word to complete each sentence.**

1. The ship's commander told the sailors what to do.

2. The amount of gravity on the moon let astronauts run very fast.

3. Carrying a heavy backpack puts pressure on your shoulders.

4. The astronaut collected rock samples on the moon.

5. Neptune is a gigantic planet.

6. Spacecrafts sometimes orbit Earth.

Apply **Read each clue. Write the correct vocabulary word in the boxes. When you have written all the words, write each circled letter in the matching numbered blank to answer the riddle below.**

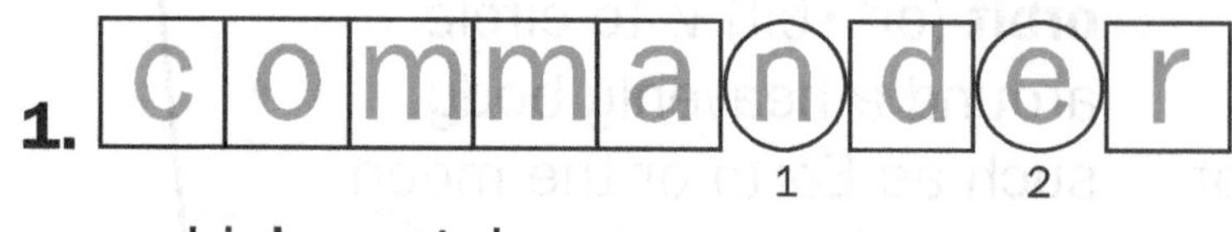

1. commander

a ship's captain

2. pressure

the push of a weight

3. orbit (4)

to go around Earth

4. astronaut (5)

a person trained to go into space

5. gigantic (6)

very big

6. gravity

the force that pulls you toward Earth

What kind of music do planets like to listen to?

n e p - t u n e s
1 2 3 - 4 5 6 2 7

Name ______________________ Date __________

Taking Notes in an Outline

Use the outline below to take notes from "Journey to the Moon." Write down the main ideas and supporting details.

Answers will vary.

I. "Journey to the Moon"

A. Apollo 11 mission

1. made of two parts, the Columbia and the Eagle

2. the Eagle landed on the moon July 20, 1969

3. returned to Earth July 24, landed in the Pacific Ocean

B. the moon

1. empty, stark, made of rock and sand

2. weak gravity

3. no weather on the moon

Taking Notes in an Outline (continued)

You read and outlined "Journey to the Moon." As you outlined, you took notes about what you read. **Use your outline on the previous page and your knowledge of the story to answer the following questions.**

What was your investigation question?

Why don't people live on the moon?

What was your conjecture about your investigation question?

People don't live on the moon because it is too far away.

Does any information in "Journey to the Moon" relate to your conjecture? yes

If so, how? If not, why not?

The story tells about how far the moon is from Earth. It also tells about how the moon has weak gravity, no sun, and nothing grows there. Those things make the moon a bad place to live.

Name ______________________ Date __________

Writing a Persuasive Paragraph

Audience: Who will read your persuasive paragraph?

Possible Answer people in my school

Purpose: What is your purpose for writing the paragraph?

Possible Answer I want to convince people that our school should start a recycling program.

Prewriting **Use this organizer to help you plan your persuasive paragraph.** **Possible Answers**

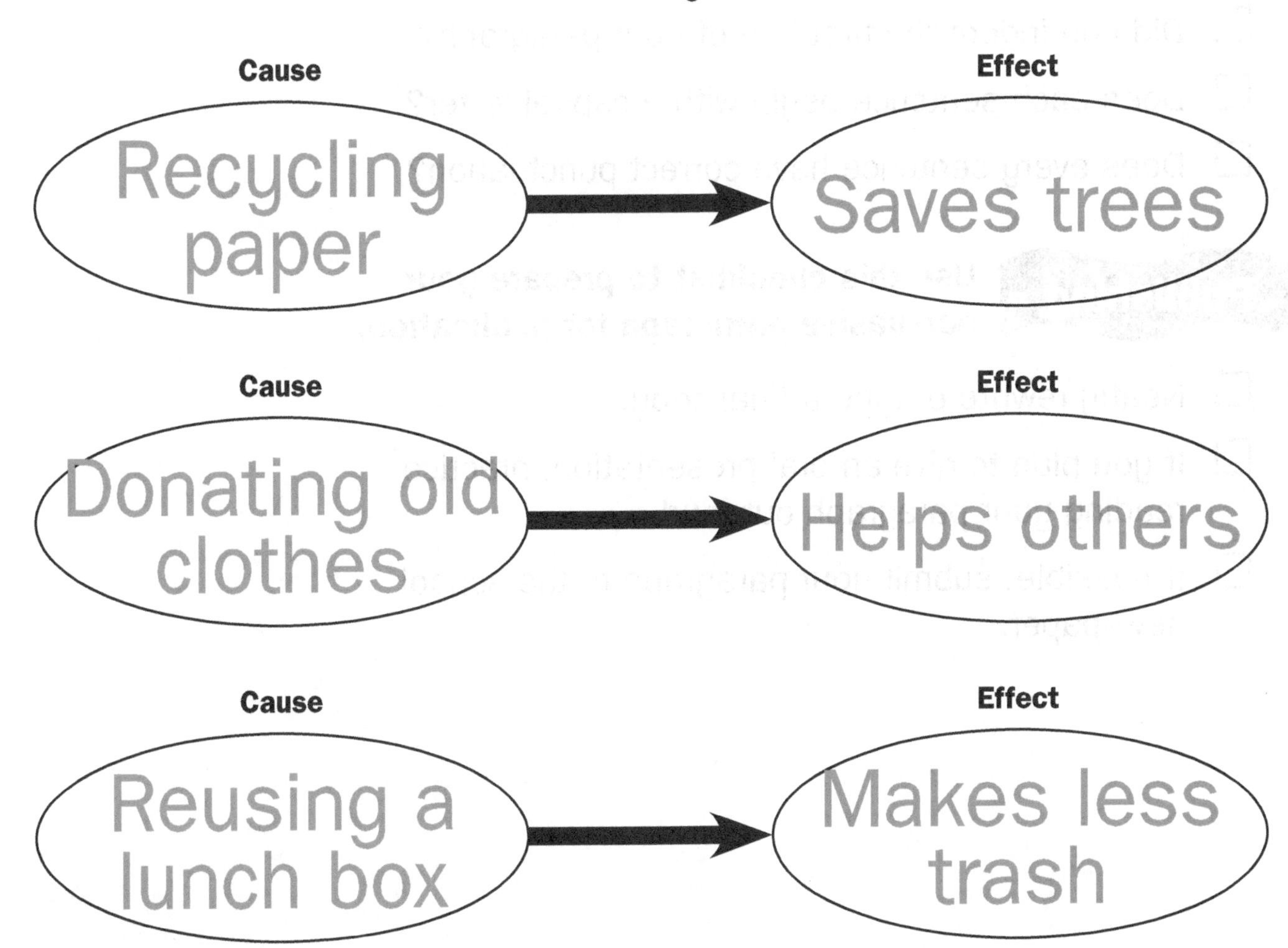

Revising

Use this checklist to revise your persuasive paragraph.

- ☐ Is your main idea clearly stated?
- ☐ Do your facts and feelings support your main idea?
- ☐ Is your most convincing detail in the last sentence?
- ☐ Are your reasons or facts true?

Editing/Proofreading

Use this checklist to correct mistakes.

- ☐ Did you use correct spellings?
- ☐ Did you indent the first line of your paragraph?
- ☐ Does each sentence begin with a capital letter?
- ☐ Does every sentence have correct punctuation?

Publishing

Use this checklist to prepare your persuasive paragraph for publication.

- ☐ Neatly rewrite or type a final copy.
- ☐ If you plan to give an oral presentation, practice reading your paragraph out loud.
- ☐ If possible, submit your paragraph to the school newspaper.

UNIT 4 Lesson 4

Name ______________________ Date __________

Spelling

Focus Latin roots are word parts derived from Latin that have certain meanings.

The root ***grat*** means "thankful or pleasing."
The root ***mar*** means "sea or ocean."
The root ***miss*** (sometimes spelled *mit*) means "sent."
The root ***port*** means "carry."

Greek roots are word parts derived from Greek that have certain meanings.
The root ***ast*** means "star."
The root ***graph*** means "something written or drawn."
The root ***log*** (sometimes spelled *logue*) means "to speak."
The root ***scop*** means "to look at or examine."

Word List

1. grateful
2. mission
3. report
4. autograph
5. astronaut
6. dialogue
7. import
8. marine
9. photograph
10. mariner
11. dismiss
12. gratitude
13. astronomy
14. apology
15. telescope

Challenge Words

16. biography
17. microscope

Practice **Sort the spelling words under the correct heading.**
Order will vary under heading.

Latin root *grat*

1. grateful
2. gratitude

Latin root *mar*

3. marine
4. mariner

Latin root *miss*

5. mission
6. dismiss

Latin root *port*

7. report
8. import

Greek root *ast*

9. astronaut
10. astronomy

Greek root *graph*

11. autograph
12. photograph

Greek root *log*

13. dialogue
14. apology

Greek root *scop*

15. telescope

Name ______________________ Date __________

Synonyms and Antonyms

Synonyms are words with the same or nearly the same meaning. A dictionary or thesaurus can help you find synonyms for many words.

Example: Cheerleaders scream and clap for the team.
Cheerleaders shout and clap for the team.
(*Shout* and *scream* are synonyms.)

Antonyms are words with opposite meanings. Sometimes a thesaurus will list some antonyms of a word after its synonyms.

Example: She smiled because she was happy.
She frowned because she was sad.
(*Happy* and *sad* are antonyms.)

Read the following sentence from "Journey to the Moon." Then, answer the questions below.

Possible Answers

But the astronauts were very excited.

1. *Excited* means "filled with a strong feeling or emotion." What emotion were the astronauts feeling in the sentence?
   happiness

2. Sometimes a synonym cannot replace the word in a sentence. The word *upset* is a synonym of *excited.* Why would this synonym not make sense in the above sentence?
   The astronauts were not upset; they were happy.

Lesson 4

Read the following sentences from "Journey to the Moon." Then answer the questions below.

Possible Answers

After only two-and-a-half hours on the moon, the two astronauts were exhausted. They had been awake for 22 hours when they climbed back into the Eagle.

3. Write a clue from the sentences that could help you know what *exhausted* means.

They had been awake for 22 hours.

4. Look up two synonyms for the word *exhausted* in a thesaurus or dictionary. Write the words below.

tired   beat

5. Substitute one of your synonyms for *exhausted* in the sentence.

After only two-and-a-half hours on the moon, the two astronauts were tired.

6. Look up two antonyms for *exhausted.*

energized   refreshed

7. Substitute one of your antonyms for *exhausted* in the sentence below.

After only two-and-a-half hours on the moon, the two astronauts were refreshed.

Explain how the antonym changes the sentence's meaning.

It changes the sentence by making it say that they had lots of energy.

Lesson 4

Name ______________________ Date __________

Note Taking

Note taking means writing down ideas as you learn them.

Read the paragraph and the questions that follow it. Fill in the circle next to the best answer to each question.

Hieroglyphics is a system of writing in which pictures are used instead of words or letters. The Egyptians are the most famous users of hieroglyphics. Other people, like the Maya, also used hieroglyphics. Scientists believe the Egyptians began using hieroglyphics more than 5,000 years ago. Hieroglyphics were carved on stone or written on something like paper. We can understand hieroglyphics because of the Rosetta Stone. This stone has hieroglyphics and other languages on it. People were able to translate from the hieroglyphics to the other languages.

1. If you were taking notes about the meaning of the word *hieroglyphics,* which of these would be most important?

○ Egyptians used hieroglyphics.

● Hieroglyphics is a form of picture writing.

○ Sometimes hieroglyphics were carved on stone.

2. If you were taking notes about understanding hieroglyphics, which of these would be most important?

● The Rosetta Stone helped us understand hieroglyphics.

○ Hieroglyphics are more than 5,000 years old.

○ The Maya used hieroglyphics.

Note Taking (continued)

Reread "Journey to the Moon." Answer the questions below to practice taking notes.

3. When did the first people land on the moon? July 20, 1969

4. Who were the astronauts? Neil Armstrong, Edwin "Buzz" Aldrin, and Michael Collins

5. Write down the names of the following, and describe what they did:

- the command module Columbia; it orbited the moon
- the lunar module the Eagle; it landed on the moon

6. Write down some words to help you remember what the moon was like.
Possible Answers no houses, no trees, rocks, sand, empty, weak gravity

7. How long were the astronauts on the moon? two and a half hours

8. Look back over the notes you took. What other ideas from the story might be important to remember? **Possible Answers** who was president, what happened after the astronauts came back, what they did on the moon

Name ______________________ Date __________

Review of *-ly, -y, -ment, -tion, -ful, -able, -ed,* and *-ing*

Focus

Remember, a **suffix** is a word ending.

- ***-ly*** changes a word into an adverb. (light, light<u>ly</u>)
- ***-y*** changes a noun into an adjective. (shine, shin<u>y</u>)
- ***-ment*** changes a verb into a noun. It means "action" or "process." (govern, govern<u>ment</u>)
- ***-tion*** changes a verb into a noun. It means "action" or "process." (invent, inven<u>tion</u>)
- ***-ful*** changes a noun into an adjective. It means "full of." (sorrow, sorrow<u>ful</u>)
- ***-able*** changes a verb or noun into an adjective. It means "able or tending to be" something. (read, read<u>able</u>)

Remember, the **inflectional endings** *-ed* and *-ing* change the tense of a verb.

- The ***-ed*** ending shows an action that happened in the past.
- The ***-ing*** ending shows an action that is happening now.

Practice **Circle the correct spelling of each word below.**

1. claped clapped
2. shady shadey
3. relatetion relation
4. saying saiing

Lesson 5

Use a word from the box to complete each sentence below.

useful	argument	adorable	collection
curly	swimming	smoothly	

5. The girl had long, curly hair.
6. A hammer is a useful tool for pounding nails.
7. The water flowed smoothly and swiftly down the falls.
8. The brothers got into an argument about whose turn it was.
9. The adorable baby made everyone smile.
10. The team is swimming laps in the pool.
11. I have a collection of old comic books.

Circle the ending on each word below. Correctly use the word in a sentence of your own.

12. joy(ful) **Possible Answer** The joyful girl jumped up and down.
13. quiet(ly) **Possible Answer** The mouse walked quietly.
14. dirt(y) **Possible Answer** The boy washed the dirty clothes.

Name ______________________ Date __________

Review of *-ity, -less, -ness, -sion,* and Greek and Latin Root Words

Focus

Remember that **suffixes** are word endings.

- ***-ity*** changes an adjective into a noun. It means "state of being." (real, real<u>ity</u>)
- ***-less*** changes a noun into an adjective. It means "without" or "not having." (worth, worth<u>less</u>)
- ***-ness*** changes an adjective into a noun. It means "state of being." (kind, kind<u>ness</u>)
- ***-sion*** changes a verb into a noun. It means "action" or "process." (discuss, discus<u>sion</u>)

Greek and Latin roots are word parts that have certain meanings.

ast means "star"; ***graph*** means "something written or drawn"; ***log*** (sometimes spelled *logue*) means "to speak"; ***scop*** means "to look at or examine"; ***grat*** means "thankful or pleasing"; ***mar*** means "sea or ocean"; ***miss*** (sometimes spelled *mit*) means "sent"; ***port*** means "carry"

Practice

Circle the suffix or root in each word below. Complete the word's definition using what you know about the suffix or root.

1. simplicity: "the state of being simple"

2. gratitude: "the state of being thankful"

3. gentleness: "the state of being gentle"

4. hopeless: "without hope"

5. import: "to carry or bring things into a country"

Apply **Use a word from the box to complete each sentence.**

telescope	astronaut	autograph	prologue
decision	marine	mission	scentless

6. An astronaut was the first person to walk on the moon.

7. A whale is called a marine mammal because it lives in the sea.

8. I finally made a decision to buy a new hat.

9. The author wrote her autograph inside the book.

10. A good telescope can help you see Saturn's moons.

11. The explorer was sent on a mission to find gold.

12. Gwen could not smell the flower because it was scentless.

13. The actor gave the prologue before the play started.

UNIT 4 Lesson 5

Name ______________________ Date __________

Selection Vocabulary

Focus

scale (skāl) *n.* the size of a map, picture, or model compared with what it represents (page 100)

astronomers (as · tron' · əm · ûrz') *n.* plural form of **astronomer:** someone who studies stars (page 101)

atmosphere (at' · məs · fēr') *n.* area of gas surrounding a planet (page 108)

curve (kûrv) *n.* a bending line (page 102)

top (top) *n.* a spinning toy (page 104)

rotation (rō · tā' · shən) *n.* motion about a center point, or an axis (page 104)

scraped (skrāpd) *v.* past tense of **scrape:** to push or pull an object over another (page 109)

signs (sīnz) *n.* plural form of **sign:** a trace (page 111)

Practice

Match each vocabulary word with its clue.

1. atmosphere

2. top

3. scale

4. rotation

5. signs

a. This surrounds Earth.

b. You do this when you ride on a merry-go-round.

c. This is a twirling toy.

d. Footprints in the snow are an example of these.

e. This is the size difference between a map and the place it shows.

Apply **The underlined vocabulary words have gotten mixed up. Cross out each incorrect word, and write the correct word beneath the sentence.**

6. Long ago, sailors noticed Earth's horizon was shaped like a ~~top~~.

 curve

7. This helped people realize Earth was round and spun like a ~~scale~~.

 top

8. They learned that Earth's ~~atmosphere~~ makes day and night.

 rotation

9. ~~Signs~~ have been able to learn more about our solar system.

 Astronomers

10. The air in our ~~rotation~~ keeps us alive.

 atmosphere

11. They have, however, found ~~astronomers~~ of water on Mars.

 signs

12. Long ago, water may have ~~curve~~ stones across Mars, making river beds.

 scraped

13. As they learn more, they can make Mars maps to ~~scraped~~.

 scale

Name ______________________ Date __________

Timed Writing

Audience: Who will read your writing on a timed test?

Possible Answer people who are grading the test

Purpose: What is your reason for writing this composition?

Possible Answer I want to show that I can follow directions and write quickly.

Prewriting

Use these reminders as you write your timed composition.

- Write about your favorite animal or a special pet you have.
- Explain why you like it or give details about the pet.
- Make sure that each sentence you write helps the reader understand your composition.
- Make sure that your ideas are clear and easy for the reader to follow.
- Check your work for correct spelling, capitalization, punctuation, grammar, and sentence structure.

Revising

Use this checklist to revise your composition.

- ☐ Did you underline each thing you were asked to write about in the reminders?
- ☐ Did you make notes before writing?
- ☐ Did you respond to each reminder?

Editing/Proofreading

Use this checklist to correct mistakes.

- ☐ Did you indent your paragraphs?
- ☐ Did you use correct spellings?
- ☐ Did you capitalize the first word of each sentence?
- ☐ Did you end each sentence with correct punctuation?

Name ______________________ Date __________

Spelling

Focus Remember the skills you have learned from Unit 4.

The suffixes ***-ly, -y, -ment, -ful, -able, -ity, -less, -ness,*** and ***-sion*** can be added to the end of a word to change the meaning of the word.

When the inflectional ending ***-ing*** is added to a base verb it shows that the action is happening now. Inflectional ending ***-ed*** shows that the action happened in the past.

Some words are derived from **Latin** and **Greek roots.**

Word List

1. scary
2. kindly
3. pleasing
4. clogged
5. harmful
6. erosion
7. careless
8. statement
9. mariner
10. grateful
11. import
12. notable
13. electricity
14. weakness
15. telescope

Challenge Words

16. advertisement
17. amusing

Practice **Sort the spelling words under the correct heading.**

Order will vary under heading.

Suffix *-ly*

1. kindly

Dropped e, added suffix *-y*

2. scary

Suffix *-ment*

3. statement

Dropped *de*, added suffix *-sion*

4. erosion

Spelling (continued)

Suffix *-ful*

5. harmful

Dropped e, added suffix *-able*

6. notable

Suffix *-ity*

7. electricity

Suffix *-less*

8. careless

Suffix *-ness*

9. weakness

Dropped e, added inflectional ending *-ing*

10. pleasing

Doubled consonant, added inflectional ending *-ed*

11. clogged

Latin and Greek roots

12. mariner
13. grateful
14. import
15. telescope

Name ______________________ Date __________

Subject/Verb Agreement

Focus A singular subject requires a singular verb, and a plural subject requires a plural verb. Sometimes the verb changes its form depending on whether the subject is singular or plural.

Rule	Example
• If the subject is singular, the present tense form of the verb usually ends in *-s* or *-es.*	• **He saves** his money in a cookie jar.
• If the subject is plural, do not add anything to the verb to form the present tense.	• **They invest** money for a living.
• If the verb ends with a consonant and *y,* change the *y* to *i* and add *-es* to create the present tense.	• **hurry + -es = hurries**
• In the present tense, the irregular verbs *be* and *have* change forms to agree with their subjects.	• **Danny is** responsible with money, but his **friends are** not. **Danny has** $10 left, but his **friends have** only $1.

Practice **Circle the verb that agrees with the subject.**

1. He **is/are** opening a bank account tomorrow.

2. You **has/have** forgotten your gym clothes again!

3. The river **flow/flows** past the oak tree.

UNIT 4 Lesson 5

Apply **Choose the correct verb for each sentence and write it on the line.**

4. Lee and Lisa ___are___ ten years old. (are, is)

5. Lee and Lisa ___have___ a savings account. (have, has)

6. Lee ___puts___ $10 in their account each week.
(puts, put)

7. He ___marches___ right up to the bank teller. (march, marches)

8. Saving money ___teaches___ good money management. (teach, teaches)

Circle the verbs that do not agree with their subjects. Write the correct verb at the end of the sentence. Write *correct* if the verb is correct.

9. Shakespeare (are) the author of the play called *Hamlet*. ___is___

10. The play (have) a character named Horatio. ___has___

11. Horatio is a friend of Hamlet. ___correct___

12. Hamlet's father (were) the king. ___was___

13. Horatio (give) advice to Hamlet. ___gives___

Name ______________________ Date __________

Using a Glossary

Focus A **glossary** is a special section at the end of a book. It can help you find some words' meanings, spellings, and pronunciations. It may also tell you on what pages each word is used.

- The words in a glossary are listed in ABC order. They are called **entry words.**
- If a glossary is longer than a page, the top of each page has two words. These are called **guide words.**
  - The word on the left is the first entry word on the page.
  - The word on the right is the last entry word on the page.
  - All the words on the page fall in ABC order between these two guide words.

Practice **Look up the following words from "Earth" in the glossary at the back of your book. Write the guide words for each word.**

1. brave bald carpenters
2. rotation recollections section
3. vegetation top voyage
4. orbit modern penetrate
5. signs setting squinty

Lesson 5

The following shows the top of a glossary page. Use it to answer the questions below.

Broil **Curve**

broil (broi' əl) *v.* **To make very hot.** *We sometimes broil steaks to cook them.* **(page 356)**

bushy (bu' shē) *adj.* **Shaggy and thick.** *The dog had thick, bushy hair.* **(page 356)**

6. What is the first word on this glossary page? broil
7. What is the last word on this glossary page? curve
8. How do you know what the last word is if you cannot see the bottom of the page? I can see the guide words.
9. What does (broi' əl) tell you? It tells you how to pronounce broil.
10. What does *adj.* tell you about the word *bushy*?

    It tells you the word is an adjective.
11. What does (page 356) tell you about *broil*?

    It tells you on what page the word is used.
12. What does *Shaggy and thick* tell you about bushy?

    It is the definition.
13. Why is *bushy* listed after *broil* on the page?

    Glossary words are listed in ABC order.

Name ______________________ Date __________

Prefixes *re-* and *un-*

Focus

The prefix ***re-*** means "again."

build ("to form using materials") ⟶ **rebuild** ("to build again")

The prefix ***un-*** means "not" or "to do the opposite of."

painted ("covered with paint") ⟶ **unpainted** ("not covered with paint")

fold ("to lay one part over another") ⟶ **unfold** ("to do the opposite of folding")

Practice

Read each definition below. Use *re-* and *un-* to write a word that matches each definition.

1. "named again" renamed
2. "not open" unopened
3. "not wanted" unwanted
4. "to freeze again" refreeze
5. "to drill again" redrill
6. "not paved" unpaved
7. "not safe" unsafe
8. "to learn again" relearn
9. "not afraid" unafraid
10. "to introduce again" reintroduce

Use the words you made on the previous page to complete the sentences below.

11. Long ago trails and streets were unpaved.

12. You can sometimes find old unwanted or lost arrowheads buried in the ground.

13. People have changed the old names of cities and renamed them.

14. It is unsafe to sleep near a lit campfire.

15. When you open an unopened jar, the lid often makes a popping sound.

16. Jenna had forgotten the boy's name, so he had to reintroduce himself.

17. The girl listened to the scary story, but she was unafraid.

18. I had to relearn horseback riding because I'd forgotten how to do it.

19. The ice cream had melted a little, so we had to refreeze it in the freezer.

20. Adam had to redrill the hole to fit the bigger screw.

Name ______________________ Date __________

Prefixes *pre-* and *mis-*

Focus

The prefix ***pre-*** means "before" or "ahead of."

bake ("to cook in an oven") ⟶ **prebake** ("to cook in an oven ahead of time")

The prefix ***mis-*** means "wrong" or "bad."

match ("to put similar things together") ⟶ **mismatch** ("to put the wrong things together")

Practice **Add the given prefix to each word below. Write the new word and the meaning of the new word on the lines.**

	Prefix	Word	New Word/New Meaning
1.	*mis-*	write	miswrite; to write something wrong
2.	*mis-*	cut	miscut; to cut something wrong
3.	*pre-*	chill	prechill; to chill something ahead of time
4.	*pre-*	game	pregame; before the game
5.	*mis-*	shapen	misshapen; badly shaped

Lesson 1

Write sentences using two of the words you made on the previous page. Possible Answers

6. We had a pregame party.
____

7. I miscut the shape of my picture.
____

Circle the word that correctly completes each sentence below.

8. Abby had one red and one blue sock on because she had _______________ her socks.
   (a.) mismatched   b. premade

9. The oven was already hot because it was _______________.
   a. prefrozen   (b.) preheated

10. I rinse and _______________ the dishes before putting them in the dishwasher.
   a. prewrap   (b.) prewash

11. Sonja called the wrong phone number because she _______________.
   (a.) misdialed   b. pretaped

12. The boys got lost because they _______________ their walk.
   a. preplanned   (b.) misplanned

Name ______________________________ Date ____________

Selection Vocabulary

Focus

fierce (fērs) *adj.* strong and wild; raging (page 131)

sturdy (stûr' • dē) *adj.* strong; hardy (page 131)

stump (stump) *n.* part of tree left over after cutting away at the trunk (page 134)

settlers (set' • tlûrz) *n.* plural form of **settler:** a person who makes a new home in a new land or country (page 135)

burrows (bûr' • rowz) *n.* plural form of **burrow:** a hole in the ground where some animals live (page 135)

trickle (trik' • əl) *n.* a small amount (page 140)

crumbling (krum' • bəl • ing) *v.* a form of the verb **crumble:** to fall to pieces (page 141)

treasures (trezh' • ûrz) *n.* plural form of **treasure:** something special; a keepsake (page 143)

Practice **Circle the vocabulary word that matches each group of underlined words.**

1. When people from England first moved to America, they built small towns.
   a. treasures **b.** settlers

2. The powerful, gushing river tossed the boat.
   a. trickle **b.** fierce

3. The dish did not break because it was strong.
   a. sturdy **b.** crumbling

4. I keep my special necklaces in a jewelry box.
   a. sturdy (b.) treasures

Apply **Use a vocabulary word to complete each sentence.**

5. In the 1800s, many settlers moved to the western United States.

6. They drove wagons over deserts and through fierce, deep rivers.

7. They brought food, tools, and a few treasures with them.

8. Some people built dugout houses, which were like large burrows for people.

9. Others built sturdy log cabins.

10. Sometimes they made a table out of a leftover tree stump.

11. The houses were near a river, stream, or small trickle of water.

12. Most of these houses are gone now, and those that are left are crumbling.

Name ______________________ Date __________

Author's Purpose

Focus Remember, the **author's purpose** is the author's reason for writing.

- The author's purpose can be to *inform,* to *explain,* to *entertain,* or to *persuade.*
- An author can have more than one purpose.
- The purpose affects the details, descriptions, story events, and dialogue.

Practice **Read each group of sentences below. Write the author's purpose on the line.**

1. First, roll out the biscuit dough. Next, cut a two-inch circle from the dough. Finally, place the dough on the baking sheet.

   Author's Purpose: to explain

2. I am always doing things that embarrass me. The other day, I was eating lunch with my friends when Karl said something really funny just as I took a drink of milk. I started laughing, and suddenly, milk came out of my nose!

   Author's Purpose: to entertain

3. People need to make healthful food choices. Fruits, vegetables, and whole grains keep your heart healthy and make you feel good. Sugary snacks are not good fuel for your body.

   Author's Purpose: to persuade

UNIT 5 Lesson 1

Read the following sentences from "The House on Maple Street." Use them to answer the questions below. Possible Answers

Ruby had a set of china dishes that she played with every day. One day when she was making a mud pie on the banks of the stream, she found an arrowhead buried deep in the ground. She put it in a cup to show her father when he came in from the fields.

4. What do you think the author's purpose is?

to entertain

5. What is one clue that helped you decide?

The author is telling an interesting story about how Ruby found an arrowhead.

6. Reread the whole story. What could another purpose be?

to explain

7. What is one clue that helped you decide?

The author is explaining how an arrowhead and cup got somewhere.

Write a short paragraph that tells the reader about something that happened at your school. Its purpose should be to inform.

8. Last week a theater group came to our school. They performed the play "Snow White." It was really funny. Afterward the actors answered questions. I enjoyed the play.

Name ______________________ Date ________

Generating Ideas and Questions about Your Community

What is special about your community? What things does your community have that others don't?

Our neighborhood has a school, a market, a fire station, and a public library. In our community, we can walk to the store, to the library, and to school.

List things you think are interesting about your community.

Our neighborhood is very old. It is full of many different people. We have six churches. We have many different restaurants and three festivals every year.

List things that you want to know more about in your community.

What is the history of the neighborhood? Who discovered our community? Why do we have so many restaurants? What is the history of our festivals?

Generating Ideas and Questions about Your Community (continued)

These are things about your community's past that would be fun or interesting to research:

When did the festivals begin? Who started them? Why do we have six churches? Are they old? When was our community started?

How might things you find out about your community's past be useful or valuable to the class and others?

Many neighborhoods are different but some are alike. Others may not have asked the same questions that we did. Maybe they will want to ask different questions about their communities.

Name ______________________ Date __________

Writing a Persuasive Paragraph Possible Answers

Audience: Who will read your persuasive paragraph?

people in my school

Purpose: What is your purpose for writing the paragraph?

I want to convince students at my school to make a time capsule.

Use this organizer to help you plan your persuasive paragraph. Possible Answers

Main Idea

We should make a time capsule.

Detail

People like to learn about the past.

Detail

We can show people in the future what kids used to do.

Detail

Time capsules are fun to make.

Revising

Use this checklist to revise your persuasive paragraph.

- ☐ Is your main idea clearly stated?
- ☐ Do your facts and feelings support your main idea?
- ☐ Is your most convincing detail in the last sentence?
- ☐ Are your reasons or facts true?

Editing/Proofreading

Use this checklist to correct mistakes.

- ☐ Did you use correct spelling?
- ☐ Did you indent the first line of your paragraph?
- ☐ Does each sentence begin with a capital letter?
- ☐ Does every sentence have correct punctuation?

Publishing

Use this checklist to prepare your persuasive paragraph for publication.

- ☐ Neatly rewrite or type a final copy.
- ☐ If you plan to give an oral presentation, practice reading your paragraph out loud.
- ☐ If possible, submit your paragraph to the school newspaper.

Name ______________________ Date __________

Spelling

Focus A word changes meaning when a prefix is added to the beginning of the word.

The prefix ***re-*** means "again."

The prefix ***un-*** means "not" or "opposite of."

The prefix ***pre-*** means "before."

The prefix ***mis-*** means "wrong" or "bad."

Word List

1. mismatch
2. unclear
3. reread
4. refund
5. unzip
6. misprint
7. unload
8. mislead
9. preheat
10. restart
11. prefix
12. unfair
13. recount
14. misplace
15. preview

Challenge Words

16. preschool
17. unaware

Practice **Sort the spelling words under the correct heading.**

Order will vary under heading.

Prefix *re-*

1. reread
2. refund
3. restart
4. recount

Prefix *un-*

5. unclear
6. unzip
7. unload
8. unfair

Spelling (continued)

Prefix *pre-*

9. preheat
10. prefix
11. preview

Prefix *mis-*

12. mismatch
13. misprint
14. mislead
15. misplace

Name ______________________ Date __________

Verb Tenses

A **verb tense** tells whether the action is happening in the present, happened in the past, or will happen in the future.

Present tense verbs show what is happening right *now,* or what *always* happens.
Example: Monica loves the musical *My Fair Lady.* She is singing in the living room.

Add ***-ed*** to the present tense form of most verbs to show **past tense.** Not all verbs form the past tense by adding *-ed.*
Example: Phil wrote his report, while his father painted the house.

The **future tense** is formed by using the helping verb *will.*
Example: People will travel to Mars someday.

Write *past, present,* or *future* to identify the tense of the boldfaced verb in each sentence.

1. I **will go** to Chicago this summer. future
2. Chicago **is** a very old city. present
3. A fire in 1871 **burned** much of the city. past
4. People **rebuilt** the city. past
5. I **will see** all the sights there. future

UNIT 5 Lesson 1

Apply **Circle verbs in the past tense. (Remember, not all of them end in *-ed.*)**

On Saturday, we drove to the animal shelter. I immediately saw the cat I wanted. He was an orange bundle of fur. "That's the one I want," I said. My parents weren't sure, but then I said, "I will take care of him. I will feed him every day." After the veterinarian gave the kitten shots, we took him home with us. I named him Tiger because of his orange stripes.

The writer of the passage below made some verb mistakes. In each blank, write the correct tense of the underlined verb.

When Sally Lin comes home from school, her mom was is at work. Mrs. Lin always left leaves a key for Sally so she can get in the house.

One day, however, was different. Sally got home and saw that her mom forgets forgot to leave the key. Sally is was not scared. She thought to herself, "I knew know what to do. I went will go to the McCarthys' house next door. Mom told me to ask them for help if I ever needed it."

Name ______________________ Date ____________

Internet Searches

Focus

Logical operators are simple words (commands) used to make your internet search more specific.

The most commonly used operators are ***and, or,*** and ***quotation marks.***

How It Works

- If you are looking for information on tribes in Washington, then enter **tribes AND Washington.** The search engine will then look for sources that have both of these words.
- If you are looking for information on Adena and Blackfoot Indians, enter **Adena OR Blackfoot,** and the search engine will pull up sources with one or the other term (instead of only those sources that contain both words).
- Put quotation marks around specific names. For example, to find information on Flint Ridge, enter **"Flint Ridge"** in the search box of the search engine. (Otherwise, the search engine will show you all the articles that have the words *flint* and *ridge* in them. That can mean a lot of searching!)

Lesson 1

Practice coming up with keywords and using logical operators. Read the following items and fill in the blanks.

1. You are looking for information about the growing season of Washington apples.

   Keywords: Washington apples

   Logical Operator: "Washington apples"

2. You are looking for folklore from Brittany.

   Keywords: folklore Brittany

   Logical Operator: folklore and Brittany

3. You would like more information about totem poles.

   Keywords: totem poles

   Logical Operator: "totem poles"

4. You would like to learn about tribes from the Ohio Valley.

   Keywords: tribes Ohio Valley

   Logical Operator: tribes and "Ohio Valley"

5. You would like more information on the Pacific and Atlantic Oceans.

   Keywords: Pacific Atlantic Ocean

   Logical Operator: "Pacific Ocean" or "Atlantic Ocean"

Name ______________________ Date __________

The Prefixes *bi-* and *mid-*

Focus

The prefix ***bi-*** means "two."

color ("a hue or tint") ⟶ **<u>bi</u>color** ("having two colors")

The prefix ***mid-*** means "being the part in the middle."

day ("the time of light between one night and the next") ⟶ **<u>mid</u>day** ("the time in the middle of a day")

Practice **Add a prefix so each word matches the definition below.**

1. midweek week ("the middle of the week")
2. midtown town ("the middle of town")
3. bicycle cycle ("a riding machine with two wheels and pedals")
4. midwinter winter ("the middle of winter")
5. bilevel level ("having two levels")
6. midyear year ("the middle of the year")

Answer the questions below.

7. The word *annual* means "something that happens every year." What word means "something that happens twice a year"?

biannual

8. If you have one house on the East Coast and one house on the West Coast, you are bicoastal. Explain what *bicoastal* means.

It means you live on two coasts.

9. The word *biweekly* confuses people. It can mean two different things. Explain what those two things are. (Hint: think about the meaning of *bi-*.)

It could mean every two weeks or twice a week.

Use a word from the box to complete each sentence.

midnight	midstream	midweek	midair	midday

10. The hawk dove in midair for his prey below.

11. The beaver built the dam midstream.

12. Wednesday is midweek.

13. On New Year's Eve many people stay up until midnight.

14. The school has lunch at midday.

Name ______________________________ Date ____________

Prefixes *dis-* and *auto-*

Focus

The prefix ***dis-*** means "not" or "to do the opposite of."

agree ("to have the same opinion") ⟶ **disagree** ("to not have the same opinion")

The prefix ***auto-*** (sometimes spelled *aut-*) means "self" or "self-acting."

biography ("a person's life story") ⟶ **autobiography** ("a biography that is self-written")

Practice

Read each word below. Circle the base word. Think about the meaning of the prefix and the base word. Write the word's meaning.

1. dis(appear) to do the opposite of appearing
2. dis(believe) to not believe
3. dis(honest) not honest
4. dis(like) to not like

Match each word with its meaning below.

5. autograph
6. autopilot
7. automobile
8. autobiography

a. my life's story written by me
b. a kind of machine with four wheels made to take people places
c. a machine that steers and pilots ships or spacecraft on its own
d. someone's self-written name

Lesson 2

Use a word from the box to complete each sentence below.

dishonest	**dislikes**	**autobiography**	**disagreed**
discovered	**disinterested**	**autograph**	**autopilot**

9. Katharine Hepburn, a famous actor, wrote an autobiography called *My Life*.

10. The boring television show made me feel disinterested.

11. The brothers disagreed over who would go first.

12. A dishonest person cannot be trusted.

13. Many modern spacecrafts steer with autopilot.

14. When I opened the old box, I discovered treasures from long ago.

15. Roller coasters scare Tracy, so she dislikes them.

16. Last week, I got my favorite writer's autograph.

Name ______________________ Date __________

Selection Vocabulary

Focus

beats (bēts) *v.* a form of the verb **beat:** to come down strong and continuously (page 152)

charted (chärt' • əd) *v.* a form of the verb **chart:** to map; to show information as a picture (page 153)

laboratory (la' • brə • tor' • ē) *n.* a room for science experiments and tests (page 153)

challenge (chal' • lənj) *v.* to give the best of (page 156)

customs (kus' • təmz) *n.* plural form of **custom:** a practice that has become accepted by many people; a tradition (page 157)

developed (də • vel' • əpd) *v.* past tense of **develop:** to grow; to change (page 157)

ruin (rōō' • in) *n.* destruction, damage, or collapse (page 158)

origins (or' • ə • gənz) *n.* plural form of **origin:** the cause or source of something; what something begins as or comes from (page 158)

Practice

Synonyms are words that mean the same, or nearly the same, thing. Match each word with its synonym below.

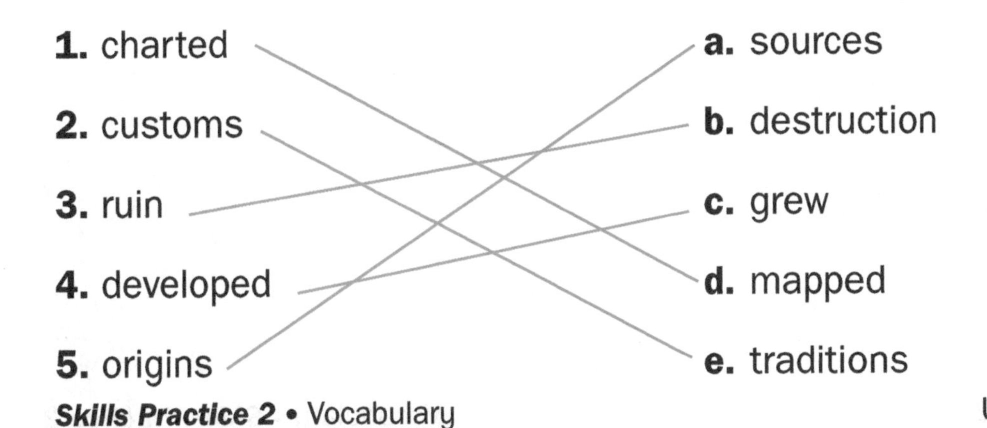

1. charted — **a.** sources

2. customs — **b.** destruction

3. ruin — **c.** grew

4. developed — **d.** mapped

5. origins — **e.** traditions

Apply

Circle the vocabulary word that completes each sentence.

6. Science has (developed/charted) over the years.
7. Long ago, archaeologists, or people who study old things, had trouble finding the (beats/origins) of artifacts.
8. Now tests in a (ruin/laboratory) can tell them the age of artifacts.
9. Studying an old (developed/ruin) of a house can tell them many things.
10. They can make good guesses about the (challenge/customs) of people who lived there.
11. They have (customs/charted) many old cities this way.
12. Archeologists like to (charted/challenge) themselves to figure out mysteries.
13. Archaeologists run for cover when rain (mapped/beats) down on their dig site.

Name ______________________ Date __________

Generating Possible Investigation Topics

An archaeologist studies past cultures and communities. If you were an archaeologist, what past cultures would you want to study? **Possible Answers**

List past societies or communities that you think would be fun to learn more about:

the Vikings, the ancient Egyptians, the ancient American Indians

What kinds of things would you like to know about those communities?

What kind of ships did Vikings have? How did the Egyptians travel? Did the American Indians live in houses?

How might knowing things about past communities help us now and in the future?

Learning how people got along and built neighborhoods in the past could help us today.

Generating Possible Investigation Topics (continued)

We can't always perfectly predict the future, but it is fun to think about. Even though we can't know what the future will bring, we can investigate what it *might* bring.

How will communities ten years from now be different? What about 100 years from now? What about a trillion years from now?

Maybe communities will be in space. Maybe in 100 years people will stop fighting and live in peace together.

How might communities use land differently in the future?

Land may not be used at all. Maybe in the future, people will use the air and build floating farms.

What are some of the problems future communities might have? How might they be able to solve these problems?

Future communities might run out of land and need to use air space for farming and living.

Name ______________________ Date __________

Writing a Persuasive Letter

Audience: Who will read your letter?

Possible Answer The person I want to convince.

Purpose: What is your reason for writing the persuasive letter?

Possible Answer I want to convince my uncle to visit me.

Use this graphic organizer to plan your persuasive letter. Write reasons that support your topic on the lines.

Possible Answers

Topic: My uncle should visit me.

- to visit the state fair
- to hear the new song I learned to play on the piano
- I miss him.
- warm weather here
- to see the rest of my family
- tour of city's historic buildings

Revising

Use this checklist to revise your persuasive letter.

- ☐ Did you write the reason for the persuasive letter?
- ☐ Did you include all of the parts of a letter?
- ☐ Did you use a variety of sentence types?
- ☐ Are the sentences in a clear order?
- ☐ Are there any words you have used too often?
- ☐ Did you use the best words to persuade?

Editing/Proofreading

Use this checklist to correct mistakes.

- ☐ Did you indent your paragraphs?
- ☐ Did you use correct verb tenses?
- ☐ Did you use correct spellings?
- ☐ Did you capitalize the greeting and the closing?
- ☐ Did you capitalize proper nouns?
- ☐ Did you end each sentence with correct punctuation?

Publishing

Use this checklist to get your persuasive letter ready to send.

- ☐ Neatly rewrite or type a final copy.
- ☐ Address an envelope.

UNIT 5 Lesson 2

Name ______________________ Date __________

Spelling

Focus **Place words** are words that reveal the location of objects within the sentence.

A word changes meaning when a prefix is added.
The prefix ***bi-*** means "every two" or "twice."
The prefix ***mid-*** means "in the middle of."
The prefix ***dis-*** means "not."
The prefix ***auto-*** means "self."

Word List

1. disprove
2. bifocal
3. autopilot
4. upon
5. midsummer
6. distrust
7. biplane
8. automatic
9. midtown
10. within
11. automobile
12. near
13. midweek
14. disband
15. bicycle

Challenge Words

16. disagree
17. autobiography

Practice **Sort the spelling words under the correct heading.**
Order will vary under heading.

Place words

1. upon
2. within
3. near

Prefix *bi-*

4. bifocal
5. biplane
6. bicycle

Spelling (continued)

Prefix *mid-*

7. midsummer
8. midtown
9. midweek

Prefix *dis-*

10. disprove
11. distrust
12. disband

Prefix *auto-*

13. autopilot
14. automatic
15. automobile

Lesson 2

Name ______________________ Date __________

Prepositions and Prepositional Phrases

Focus

Prepositions show position or direction of a noun or pronoun.

Example: Throw the ball to me. (*to* is the preposition)
The dog jumped over the fence. (*over* is the preposition)

Prepositional phrases begin with a preposition and end with a noun or pronoun.

Example: Throw the ball to me. (*to me* is the prepositional phrase)
The dog jumped over the fence. (*over the fence* is the prepositional phrase)

Practice **Circle the correct preposition in each sentence.**

1. I bought this old coin (under/on) the Internet (for/from) $25.00.
2. It is (from/on) China.
3. The person who sold it sent the coin (in/before) an envelope.
4. There are old Greek letters (on/at) it.
5. I put it (at/in) a special frame and hung it (behind/on) the wall.

Lesson 2

Circle the prepositions and underline the prepositional phrases in each sentence.

6. The city of Rome in Italy has a lot of history.
7. People have lived in that spot for thousands of years.
8. Around 800 B.C. people called the Etruscans came from the east into northern Italy.
9. The influence of Etruscan culture can be seen in Rome.
10. People still find Etruscan objects under the city.
11. There are Etruscan tombs in hillsides outside Rome.

Circle the prepositions and underline the prepositional phrases.

Maria wanted to make a family tree for her grandmother. A family tree is a chart that shows family relationships. Maria went to her grandfather's house. He told her stories. She made a list. Then she went to the craft store down the street. She bought paper and nice markers. Maria drew a big tree on the paper. She wrote names of relatives near the branches. She put the paper in a frame. When she gave the paper to her grandmother, her grandmother was very happy. Maria's grandma hung the frame on the wall.

Name ______________________ Date __________

Interviewing

When you **interview** someone, you ask him or her questions. You find out what the person knows about something.

There are three main types of questions:

- **Factual questions** have only one correct answer.
  "When were you born?"
- **Interpretive questions** have more than one answer. They still are supported by details or facts.
  "Why did you move to Aberdeen?"
- **Evaluative questions** ask for some kind of opinion. They have no wrong answers, but they can still be supported by details.
  "Why is *Charlotte's Web* your favorite book?"

Try to ask questions that begin with *who, what, where,* and *why.* Plan your questions ahead of time so you are prepared.

Practice **Match each question to the type of question it is.**

1. How old is New York City? — **a.** factual question
2. What is your favorite part of New York? — **b.** interpretive question
3. Why did the Dutch build the city? — **c.** evaluative question

Interviewing (continued)

Apply **Think about what you would like to investigate about the theme Communities Across Time. Plan a related interview. Use the graphic organizer below.**

Possible Answers

What would you like to find out?

My grandmother's first job; what farm life is like; about her wedding

What questions will you ask?

When were you born?
What do you remember about our town?
What has changed?
What has stayed the same?
What is your favorite memory of the town?

Who will you interview?

my grandmother

Name ______________________ Date __________

Affixes as Syllables

Focus An **affix** is a group of letters that are added to a base word. Prefixes and suffixes are types of affixes.

- An affix is its own syllable.
  read (one syllable) ⟶ **re** • **read** (two syllables)
- Some affixes are two syllables.
  like (one syllable) ⟶ **like** • **a** • **ble** (three syllables)

Practice **Circle the words below that have a prefix added. Underline the words that have a suffix added. Circle the number of syllables.**

Word	Number of Syllables			
1. mismatch	1	2	3	4
2. disagree	1	2	3	4
3. agreement	1	2	3	4
4. undoable	1	2	3	4
5. prebake	1	2	3	4

Apply **Read each sentence below. Circle the word that has an affix. Correctly divide the word into syllables.**

6. People in Charleston, West Virginia, are saving an unwanted, old house.
7. The Hubbard House is nearly two hundred years old.
8. A group made the decision to buy it.
9. People had thoughtlessly added on to the house.
10. Now this group is restoring it, or fixing it up.
11. They have found beautiful things.
12. A mirror kept a secret shelf unseen.
13. The secret attic room was a rarity.
14. For a little while, it was a hospital for disabled Civil War soldiers.
15. The house has many untold stories.

Name ______________________ Date __________

Affixes Used to Change Word Meaning

Focus

You have learned about the meanings of **affixes.**

- Affixes have their own meanings.

  dis- = "not" or **"the opposite of"**

- Affixes often change the meaning of a base word.

  trust ("to believe in something") ⟶ **distrust** ("to not believe in something")

Practice

Read the sentences below. Write a prefix in each blank below to change the word's meaning to match the definition.

1. *Pilot* means "a person who drives a plane or spacecraft." ____Auto____pilot means "a machine that steers a plane or spacecraft."

2. *Like* means "to prefer or enjoy something." ____Dis____like means "to not like."

3. *Biography* is "the story of someone's life." ____Auto____biography means "a person's self-written life story."

4. *Graph* is a Latin root that means "to write." ____Auto____graphed means "to have written your own name on something." It has ____three____ syllables.

Apply **Read the sentences below. Write a prefix in each blank below to change the word's meaning to match the definition.**

5. *Appear* means "to suddenly be seen."

   ___Dis___ appear means "to not be seen anymore."

6. *Agree* means "to have the same opinion."

   ___Dis___ agree means "to not agree."

7. *Mobile* means "able to be moved."

   ___Auto___ mobile means "a special four-wheeled machine that can move on its own."

Use the words you made on this page and on the previous page to complete the sentences below.

8. Yanni and her sister ___dislike___ riding in a boat because it makes them sick.

9. The magician made himself ___disappear___, and we didn't know where he went.

10. Some spacecraft are driven by ___autopilot___.

11. If my brother and I ___disagree___ about what movie to watch, we flip a coin.

12. My dad builds cars in an ___automobile___ factory.

13. I am going to write my ___autobiography___ when I am older.

14. Dave's favorite writer ___autographed___ his copy of her book.

Name ______________________ Date __________

Selection Vocabulary

Focus

clerk (klûrk) *n.* a person who sells goods or services to customers (page 168)

rumble (rum' • bəl) *n.* a heavy, deep, rolling sound (page 168)

shattered (shat' • tərd) *adj.* destroyed completely (page 171)

exactly (eg • zakt' • lē) *adv.* without any mistakes (page 174)

damaged (dam' • ijd) *v.* past tense of **damage:** to make something less valuable or useful (page 176)

tough (tuf) *adj.* hard to deal with or do; demanding (page 177)

frames (frāmz) *n.* plural form of **frame:** the skeleton of a building (page 177)

section (sek' • shən) *n.* a part of something (page 178)

Practice **Write a vocabulary word that rhymes with each underlined word to complete the limericks below.**

1. There once was a man who was rough,

   Who didn't mind work that was tough.

   But when thunder would rumble, His courage would crumble, And he'd cry, "I give up! That's enough!"

2. A worker had built up some frames
   For big houses on streets with long names.

   But then one day they shattered, And he said, "Guess it mattered That I built them with boxes from games."

Lesson 3

Apply **Circle the vocabulary word that matches each example below.**

3. Painting houses is a demanding job.
a. shattered **b.** tough

4. Carpenters put up the skeletons of buildings.
a. clerk **b.** frames

5. The storm ruined the roof on our house.
a. damaged **b.** tough

6. Laurie heard the deep sound of thunder.
a. rumble **b.** exactly

7. My mom works in a store that sells cell phones.
a. frames **b.** clerk

8. Mai copied the address without making any mistakes.
a. exactly **b.** section

9. When the glass hit the ground, it was destroyed.
a. shattered **b.** rumble

10. I live in the north part of town.
a. rumble **b.** section

Name ______________________________ Date ____________

Fact and Opinion

Focus Writers use both facts and opinions in their writing to interest and persuade their readers.

- A **fact** is a detail that is known to be true. Facts make your writing believable and give information. Facts support your opinions.
  Laura Ingalls Wilder wrote *Little House on the Prairie.* (fact)
- An **opinion** cannot be proven true or false. You can use opinions in nonfiction writing. Characters in a fictional story can have opinions, too.
  I think *Little House on the Prairie* is the best children's book. (opinion)

Practice **Next to each sentence below, write *fact* if it gives a fact. Write *opinion* if it gives an opinion.**

1. *Little House on the Prairie* tells the story of a family's move to Kansas. fact
2. It is an interesting story. opinion
3. The story takes place in the 1800s. fact
4. When she moved, Laura had two sisters. fact

Apply **Match each opinion with a supporting fact. Write the number of the supporting fact on the line beside the opinion.**

Supporting Facts

5. Many settlers died on their journey west.

6. Some people traveled to find gold.

7. The United States government gave land to some settlers.

8. Some settlers came from other countries.

Opinions

__6__ Some settlers were interested only in money.

__7__ Farmers were excited to get their own land.

__8__ It was scary to move to the United States from another country.

__5__ Settlers had to be brave.

Name ______________________ Date __________

Finding Internet Sources

Use this page to help you find Internet sources for your group investigation.

Our group's topic:

The history of our neighborhood, Clintonville.

What things on the Internet could be useful for your investigation?

	Yes	No
Historical Documents/Facts	✔	
Photos/Illustrations		✔
Community Websites		✔
Encyclopedia Information	✔	
Diagrams	✔	
Stories		

Finding Internet Sources (continued)

Useful Internet Sources we found:

Name of Webpage or Source: The Ohio Historical Society Web page

Was this source useful in your investigation? yes

Name of Webpage or Source: Clintonville Newspaper

Was this source useful in your investigation? no

Name of Webpage or Source: www.clintonville.org

Was this source useful in your investigation? yes

Name of Webpage or Source: Encyclopedia Britannica

Was this source useful in your investigation? no

Name of Webpage or Source: www.cityofcolumbus.org

Was this source useful in your investigation? yes

Name of Webpage or Source: www.clintonvilleincorporated.org

Was this source useful in your investigation? yes

Name ______________________ Date __________

Business Letter

Audience: Who will read your business letter?

Possible Answer a store owner

Purpose: What is your reason for writing the business letter?

Possible Answer I want to explain why the store should carry my favorite cereal.

Use this graphic organizer to plan your business letter.

Possible Answers

Heading 45 N. High Street
Springfield, IL 62701

Foodway Grocery Store
8989 Plain Street
Des Moines, IA 50309 **Inside Address**

Dear Sir or Madam, **Greeting**

I am writing because I would like your store to carry Whole Oats cereal. Many people like this cereal. I think many people would buy it. If you would think about carrying it, I would appreciate it. Thank you for your time. **Body**

Closing Sincerely,

Signature Tim Greenway

Revising

Use this checklist to revise your business letter.

- ☐ Did you include all of the parts of a letter?
- ☐ Did you stay on topic?
- ☐ Are the sentences in a clear order?
- ☐ Does your business letter sound serious and polite?
- ☐ Does your letter sound like you are talking to an adult whom you respect?

Editing/Proofreading

Use this checklist to correct mistakes.

- ☐ Did you use correct spellings?
- ☐ Did you capitalize the greeting and the closing?
- ☐ Did you capitalize proper nouns?
- ☐ Did you end each sentence with correct punctuation?

Publishing

Use this checklist to get your business letter ready to send.

- ☐ Neatly rewrite or type a final copy.
- ☐ Address an envelope.

Name ____________________ Date ____________

Spelling

Focus **Affixes** are suffixes and prefixes that are added to base words. They are their own syllables in words.

They are used to change the meanings of words.

Word List

1. lucky
2. unlucky
3. freeze
4. antifreeze
5. rest
6. restful
7. restless
8. fade
9. miswrite
10. count
11. discount
12. move
13. movement
14. tell
15. retell

Challenge Words

16. exactly
17. disconnect

Practice **Sort the spelling words under the correct heading.**

Order will vary under heading.

Base words

1. freeze
2. rest
3. count
4. move
5. tell
6. fade

Words with suffixes

7. lucky
8. restful
9. restless
10. movement

Spelling (continued)

Words with prefixes

11. miswrite

12. antifreeze

13. discount

14. retell

Words with suffixes and prefixes

15. unlucky

Name ______________________ Date ____________

Subject and Verb Tense Agreement

Focus Remember that **verb tenses** show whether the action in a sentence happened in the past, is happening in the present, or will happen in the future.

Past tense: A volcano destroyed the city of Pompeii.

Present tense: Pompeii is a city in Italy.

Future tense: I will travel to Italy next summer.

Practice **Read each sentence below. Decide whether the sentences are in the past, the present or the future. Write *past, present,* or *future* on the line.**

1. My puppy, Gracie, runs in the yard all day. present
2. I will take her to the park after school. future
3. We got Gracie last month from the shelter. past
4. She was the only puppy left in her litter. past
5. She is so funny when she chases my shoelaces. present
6. Sometimes she chews on the couch. present
7. My best friend has two dogs, Max and Lilly. present
8. Gracie will meet Max and Lilly on Saturday. future
9. I am excited to introduce them. present
10. Gracie will make a great pet. future

Read the passage below. The writer made three mistakes using verb tenses. Cross out each mistake, and write the correct verb above it.

will have

I think someday people in cities ~~had~~ flying cars. You

see

will ~~saw~~ these cars zooming through the air. People will be able to go anywhere in them. We will no longer use roads on the ground. Someone will have to make roads

think

in the air instead. I ~~will think~~ that this will happen. I hope that it will happen by the time I can drive!

Write three sentences. Each sentence should use the past, present, or future tense of the verb *jump*.

Possible Answers

11. (Past tense) The cat jumped over the fence.

12. (Present tense) I jump out of bed on Saturdays.

13. (Future tense) The horse will jump over the stump.

Name ______________________ Date __________

Maps

Focus

A **map** is a diagram of a place.

- Maps can show different kinds of information. Some maps show the outlines of countries. Some show where mountains are. Some show roads in a city.
- A map's legend shows symbols used on the map. It explains what each symbol means.
- A map's scale tells how much smaller the things on the map are compared with the real-life places.

Practice **Look at the map below. It shows streets in a small town. Use it to answer the questions below.**

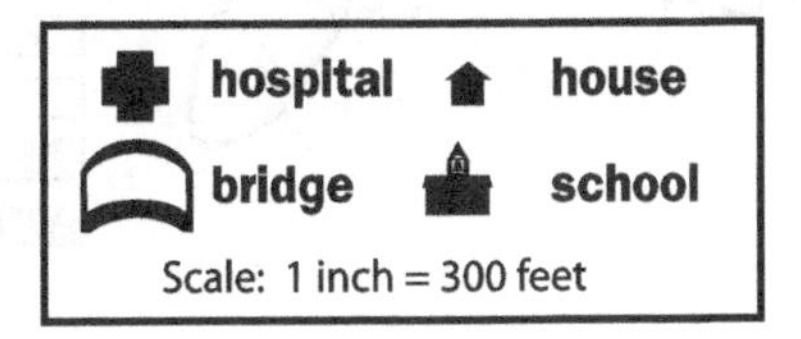

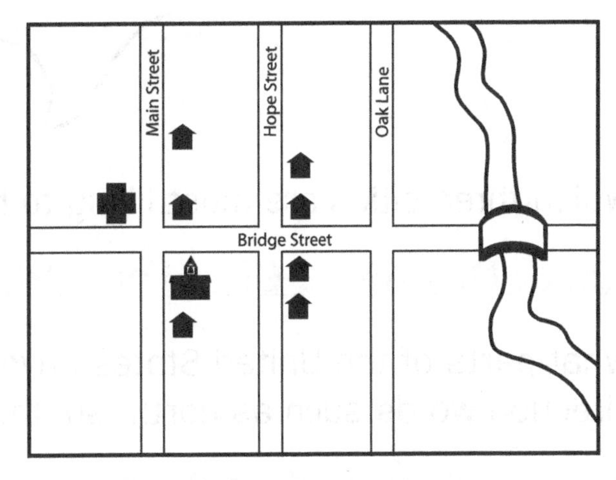

1. What street crosses Main Street? Bridge Street
2. What is the map's scale? What does it mean? 1 inch = 300 feet; 1 inch on the map equals 300 feet in the real place.
3. Where do you think Bridge Street got its name? It probably got it from the bridge it crosses outside of town.

Maps (continued)

Apply **Look at the map below. It shows tornado activity in the United States.**

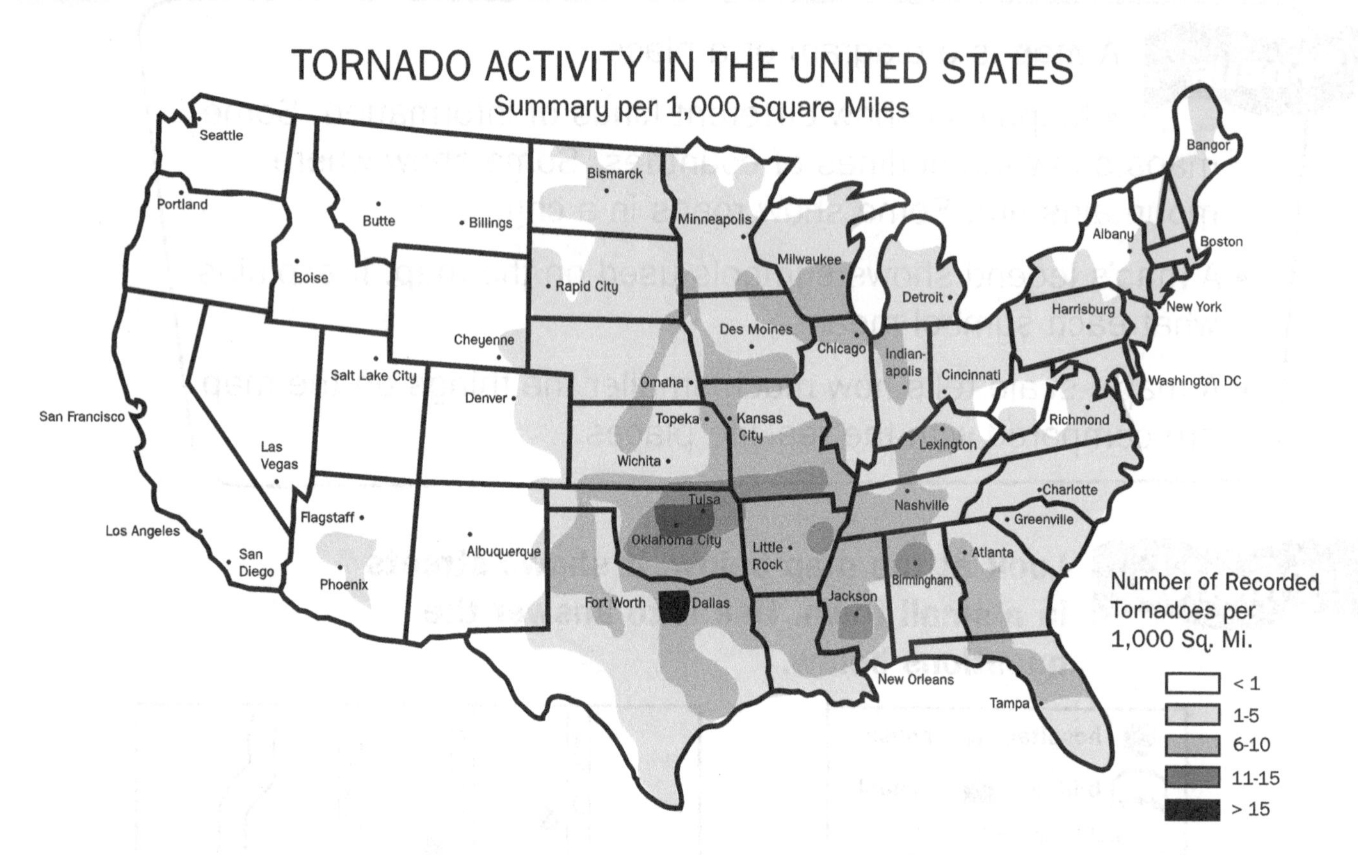

4. Which three cities are most likely to have tornadoes?

Tulsa, Oklahoma City, Forth Worth

5. What parts of the United States have the most tornadoes? (use direction words such as north, south, east, and west)

the southern and eastern parts

6. What part of the United States has almost no tornadoes?

the western part

7. What is the one city in this part of the country that does have tornadoes?

Phoenix

Name ______________________ Date __________

Word Families

Focus A **word family** is a group of words that all have the same base word.

- When you add a prefix to a base word, both words are in the same word family. ***like, dislike, unlike***
- When you add a suffix to a base word, both words are in the same word family. ***like, likely, likable***
- When you add *-ed* or *-ing* to a base word, both words are in the same word family. ***liked, liking***
- Words in a word family can have different meanings. They can be different parts of speech.

like ("to enjoy or prefer"), ***dislike*** ("to not like"),
liked (past tense of *like*)

Read the sentences below from "The Disappearing Island." Answer the questions below.

We laid out the blanket on a high sandy spot surrounded by rocks. The sand was all in long ripples made by the waves as the tide had gone out.

1. Are the words *sandy* and *sand* part of the same word family?

How do you know? Yes; I know because they share the base word sand.

2. What part of speech is *sand?* noun

3. What part of speech is *sandy?* adjective

4. What affix was added to *sand* to make *sandy?* the suffix *-y*

UNIT 5

Lesson 4

In the groups of words below, circle the two words that are in the same base word family. Write the base word of the group on the line.

				Base Word
5.	directly	undirected	dictionary	direct
6.	clown	cloudy	clouding	cloud
7.	happiness	heart	unhappy	happy
8.	dividing	division	decide	divide
9.	autopilot	pine	piloted	pilot
10.	unwise	wisely	wire	wise
11.	saddened	sorrow	sadly	sad
12.	prune	purity	purely	pure
13.	argument	arguing	angle	argue
14.	argue	disagree	agreement	agree
15.	nearly	nearing	neat	near
16.	sunny	salty	sunned	sun

Name ______________________________ Date ____________

Multisyllabic Words with Silent Consonants

Focus Some words with many syllables have silent consonants. A **silent consonant** does not add a sound to a word.

- The letter *c* is sometimes silent.

  trucking (*ck* sounds like /k/)

  science (*sc* sounds like /s/)

- The letter *k* is sometimes silent.

  knot (*kn* sounds like /n/)

- The letters *gh* are sometimes silent.

  right (*igh* sounds like / ī/)

Practice **Read each word below. Divide it into syllables. Circle it if it has a silent consonant.**

1. might|ily
2. clump|ing
3. scen|er|y
4. au|to|pi|lot
5. dark|ness
6. knit|ted

Read each sentence below. Circle any words with the silent consonants *c, gh,* or *k.*

7. When English settlers moved to America, they knew a lot.

8. They built strong houses to keep the wolves out at night.

9. They wove cloth on looms, cut it with scissors, and sewed their own clothes.

10. They raised their own chickens, pigs, and cows.

11. Their dogs helped them hunt by scenting deer.

12. Living in their new land was tricky but exciting.

Answer the questions below.

13. What silent consonant do both *knuckles* and *chuckles* have?

They both have the silent consonant *c* in them.

Which word has another silent consonant? knuckles

14. Write two sentences—one that ends with *knuckles,* and

one that ends with *chuckles.* **Possible Answer** I knock on a door with my knuckles. I hear a man inside who chuckles.

Do these sentences sound like a poem?

Yes, because they rhyme.

Name ______________________________ Date __________

Selection Vocabulary

Focus

voyage (voi' • əj) *v.* to journey by water or through space (page 188)

tide (tīd) *n.* the rise and fall of the sea (page 190)

sheltered (shel' • tûr d) *adj.* protected from danger (page 190)

ripples (rip' • pəlz) *n.* plural form of **ripple:** a design created by waves (page 192)

eroding (ə • rōd' • ing) *n.* the process of wearing or washing away slowly (page 193)

acres (ā' • kûrz) *n.* plural form of **acre:** a measurement equal to 43,560 square feet (page 194)

claim (klām) *v.* to take as one's own (page 194)

toppled (top' • pəld) *v.* past tense of **topple:** to fall or make fall forward (page 195)

Circle the word in parentheses that best fits each sentence.

1. Almost two hundred years ago, a group of Native Americans were taken on a (claim/voyage).
2. A new group of people decided to (sheltered/claim) the abandoned island.
3. Beautiful (eroding/ripples) in the sand were created by the ocean waves.
4. The (tide/toppled) pushed sand on to the island shore and created dunes.
5. One Native American woman lived there for many years, (sheltered/eroding) by the island.

Apply **Read each sentence. Answer each question by explaining the definition in your own words.**

Possible Answers

6. The river is eroding the shore. Describe what the river is doing.

   It is wearing down the shore.

7. When the ball hit the can, the can toppled. What happened to the can?

   It fell over.

8. For the Apollo 11 mission, three men took a voyage to the moon. What did the men do?

   They traveled through space to the moon.

9. The burrow sheltered the rabbits from the snow. What did the burrow do for the rabbits?

   It protected them from the snow.

10. The ripples in the sand looked like long, curving lines. What were the ripples?

    They were designs made by waves.

11. The farmer plowed two acres of land. What is an acre?

    It is a measurement equal to 43,560 square feet.

12. The tide came in and pulled apart the sand castle. What is a tide?

    It is the rise and fall of the sea.

13. Maggie decided to claim the armchair. What did Maggie do when she claimed the chair?

    She took it as her own.

Name ______________________ Date __________

Cause and Effect

The **cause** is *why* something happens. The **effect** is *what* happened.

- Think about what happens in each event in a story.
- Once you figure out *what* happened, you can see *why* it happened.
- Special clue words can help you find causes and effects. These words include *because, so, in order to, reason,* and *as a result of.*

Read the following sentence from the "The Disappearing Island." Answer the questions below.

When the sea started eroding the island, people moved off and took their houses with them.

1. What is the cause in this sentence? The sea started eroding the island.

2. What is the effect? People moved off the island.

3. Predict what might have happened if the sea had not eroded the island. **Possible Answer** The people would not have moved.

Apply **Read the following paragraph. Draw a line under clue words that show cause and effect.**

4. The population of the city kept growing. More and more buildings were built. The city kept growing farther out into the country. As a result, the deer had very little space. Because of this, the deer began looking for food in the city.

Write one cause and one effect underneath each paragraph below.

5. When the family bought the old house, they wanted to tear it down. They planned to build a new house. But then they found out how old the house was. They saw that it had beautiful wood around the windows. They found some old books in the attic. The family decided to fix up the house because it had so many stories.

One Cause: **Possible Answer** The house had many stories.

One Effect: **Possible Answer** The people decided to fix it up.

6. People noticed that there were fewer and fewer frogs in the pond every year. This made people worry that something in the water might be killing the eggs. So, they tested the water to find out what was making the frogs disappear.

One Cause: **Possible Answer** Fewer frogs were in the ponds.

One Effect: **Possible Answer** The people tested the water.

Name ______________________ Date __________

Interview Questions and Answers

Use these pages to write questions about communities that you want to ask in an interview. When you give your interview, listen carefully to the answers and record them here. **Possible Answers**

Question: What is your community like?

Answer: I live in a neighborhood where I can walk to school, to the store, and to the park. There are many different kinds of people that live in my neighborhood.

Question: How long have you lived in your community?

Answer: I have lived here since I was born. My parents moved here in 1980 from Detroit.

Interview Questions and Answers (continued)

Question: What is the best part of your neighborhood?

Answer: I love to walk my dog to the park and play with him. My neighbor has a dog too. Sometimes we walk our dogs together.

Question: What is bad about your community?

Answer: There is not much parking on our streets. Sometimes it is difficult to find a place to park the car.

Question: What is there to do in your community on Saturdays?

Answer: On Saturdays we play basketball when the weather is nice. Other people from the neighborhood have cookouts in the park. In the winters, we ice skate in the park.

Name ______________________ Date __________

Writing Directions

Audience: Who will read your directions?

Possible Answer my grandmother

Purpose: What is your purpose for writing the directions?

Possible Answer I want my grandmother to come to my class play.

Use this organizer to help you plan your directions. Write each step in order. Add more boxes if needed.

Possible Answers

From your house, go down Center Ave. Drive one mile.

↓

Turn left on Cedarwillow Ave. Drive five miles.

↓

Turn right on Park Ave. Drive less than one mile.

→

Turn right on Maize Ave.

↓

My school will be on your right. The address is 21 Maize Ave.

Revising

Use this checklist to revise your directions.

- ☐ Did you include all needed steps?
- ☐ Are the sentences in the best order?
- ☐ Did you number sentences to help your reader?
- ☐ Are your words clear and specific?

Editing/Proofreading

Use this checklist to correct mistakes.

- ☐ Did you number your sentences correctly?
- ☐ Did you use correct spellings, including the spellings of streets?
- ☐ Did you correctly spell and punctuate abbreviations?
- ☐ Did you capitalize each sentence?
- ☐ Did you use present tense verbs?
- ☐ Did you use correct direction words?
- ☐ Did you explain where the directions begin and end?

Publishing

Use this checklist to prepare your directions for publication.

- ☐ Neatly rewrite or type a final copy.
- ☐ Draw a map to help illustrate your directions.

Name ______________________ Date __________

Spelling

A **word family** is a group of words that all share the same base word.

Knowing the meaning of the base word can help you understand the meaning of the words in the word family.

Word List

1. live
2. lively
3. relive
4. living
5. honor
6. honorable
7. honest
8. honesty
9. direct
10. director
11. direction
12. indirect
13. doubt
14. doubtful
15. undoubted

Challenge Words

16. know
17. unknown
18. knowledge

Practice **Sort the spelling words under the correct heading.**

Order will vary under heading.

Word family *live*

1. live
2. lively
3. relive
4. living

Word family *honor*

5. honor
6. honorable
7. honest
8. honesty

Spelling (continued)

Word family *direct*

9. direct
10. director
11. direction
12. indirect

Word family *doubt*

13. doubt
14. doubtful
15. undoubted

Name ______________________ Date __________

Irregular Verb Tenses

Remember that verbs can show action, condition, or state of being of the subject.

- **State-of-being verbs** show the condition or state of being of the subject.

  Nicole and Diane were ready to leave.

- When a state-of-being verb connects the subject with a word in the predicate, it is called a **linking verb.**

  Noah is a good student.

- Some verbs do not follow the rules for forming past or future tenses. This is true for state-of-being verbs. State-of-being verbs change their spellings.

  I am happy. I was happy. I will be happy.

Write *yes* if the sentence has a state-of-being verb. Write *no* if the sentence does not have a state-of-being verb.

1. My grandma taught me how to paint. no

2. She is a painter. yes

3. She has been an artist for many years. yes

4. I will be an artist too, someday. yes

Fill in the missing linking verbs in the sentences below.

5. Yesterday ___was___ a great day.

6. Basil and oregano ___are___ herbs.

7. The athlete ___is___ a fast runner.

8. The 1960s and 1970s ___were___ times of change for our country.

9. ___Are___ there any pretzels left?

Read the following sentences. The writer made some verb mistakes. Write the proper tense of the underlined verbs in the blanks below.

10. Boston <u>will be</u> ___is___ an old city.

11. It <u>am</u> ___is___ full of stories.

12. The city <u>been</u> ___was___ named Boston in 1630.

13. Today, many changes <u>is being</u> ___are being___ made to the city.

14. Its art museum <u>has been</u> ___will be___ bigger in the future.

Name ______________________ Date __________

Activity Chart

A **chart** can help you organize information. A calendar is a type of chart.

- As you do your unit investigation, you can use a chart to help you keep track of what you learn.

Read the chore chart below. Answer the questions.

	Spring	Summer	Autumn	Winter
Dave	Plow the ground	Weed fields and harvest early crops	Weed fields. Harvest summer crops	Plow the ground and mix in compost
Heather	Plant summer crops	Plant autumn crops	Harvest summer crops	Plan for next year's crops

Heather and Dave have started a small farm on land that belonged to Dave's grandmother. This year, they decided to divide up the farm chores.

1. Who is going to do most of the planting?

Heather

2. When will they plant summer crops? spring

3. When will they plant autumn crops? summer

4. When do Heather and Dave work on the same chore? autumn

What is that chore? They both harvest the summer crops.

Activity Chart (continued)

Create a calendar chart to track what you are learning during your unit investigation.

Possible Answers

Changes to Three Neighborhoods in Springfield: 1900 to 2000				
	1900–1925	1925–1950	1950–1975	1975–2000
Downtown	Many people move there.	Downtown grows.	People begin to move away.	Businesses leave for suburbs.
Suburbs	Mostly farmland	People leave farms for city.	Many people move there.	Businesses move there.
Nearby Country	A few farms	People have trouble running farms.	Some people move there.	Begins to become a suburb.

5. Decide what you will show in your chart. Circle one of the following:
   a. planting chart
   b. archaeological discoveries in a certain place
   c. natural events
   (d.) how a community has changed

6. Decide if you will show seasons, months, or years on your calendar. Label the above chart, based on your choice. You may add or cross out columns or rows. Give your chart a title.

7. Record information from your investigation in the chart. You do not need to fill in all the boxes.

Name ______________________ Date __________

Review of Prefixes; Affixes as Syllables

Focus Remember, a **prefix** is added to the beginning of words.

- ***re-*** means "again." Example: *rebuild*
- ***un-*** means "not" or "the opposite of." Example: *unpainted*
- ***pre-*** means "before" or "ahead of." Example: *prebake*
- ***mis-*** means "wrong" or "bad." Example: *mismatch*
- ***bi-*** means "two." Example: *biweekly*
- ***mid-*** means "being the part in the middle." Example: *midday*
- ***dis-*** means "not" or "to do the opposite of." Example: *disagree*
- ***auto-*** (sometimes spelled *aut-*) means "self" or "self-acting." Example: *autobiography*

Prefixes and suffixes are types of **affixes.**

- An affix is its own syllable. Example: re • read
- Some affixes are two syllables. Example: like • a • ble

Practice **Divide the following words into syllables.**

1. readable
2. reality
3. unthinkable
4. mistaken

Apply **Write a word to match each definition below. Each word will have a prefix.**

5. bicycle "a riding machine with two wheels and pedals"

6. dislike "to not like"

7. preheat "to heat ahead of time"

8. reheat "to heat again"

9. midweek "the middle of a week"

10. unfinished "not finished"

11. misspoke "to have spoken wrongly"

Use three of the words you made above in sentences below.

12. **Possible Answer** Wednesday is midweek.

13. **Possible Answer** I reheat my dinner in the microwave.

14. **Possible Answer** I like riding my bicycle.

Name ______________________ Date __________

Word Families and Multisyllabic Words with Silent Consonants

Focus

Affixes have their own meanings.
Example: *dis-* means "the opposite of."

- These meanings change the meaning of a base word.

A **word family** is a group of words that all have the same base word. Words in a word family can have different meanings and can be different parts of speech.

Words are in the same word family when you:

- add a prefix to a base word.
- add a suffix to a base word.
- add *-ed* or *-ing* to a base word.

A **silent consonant** does not add a sound to a word. The letters *c, k,* and *gh* are sometimes silent.

Practice **Read each word below. Divide it into syllables. Circle any silent consonants.**

1. nightly
2. crushing
3. knitted
4. unstuck
5. autopilot
6. mistake

Lesson 5

In the groups of words below, circle the two words that are in the same word family. Write the base word of the group on the line.

				Base Word
7.	(misplaced)	(placemat)	probably	place
8.	(untied)	tilt	(necktie)	tie
9.	midyear	(weekend)	(biweekly)	week
10.	(rerun)	(running)	resting	run

Read each sentence below. Write a second sentence using the word in parenthesis. Be sure to think about the word's meaning, based on its prefix.

11. I washed the car yesterday. (rewash)

Possible Answer I rewashed the car because it was dirty again.

12. Henry ties his shoelaces when he puts on his shoes. (unties)

Possible Answer He unties them when he takes them off.

13. Last year the club met weekly. (biweekly)

Possible Answer This year they will meet biweekly.

14. The sisters usually agree. (disagree)

Possible Answer Sometimes they disagree.

Name ______________________________ Date __________

Focus

produce (prō' • do͞os) *n.* farm products, such as fresh fruits and vegetables (page 216)

seasonal (sē' • zən • əl) *adj.* ripe at a certain time (page 217)

particular (pär' • tik' • ū • lûr) *adj.* special (page 217)

necessities (nəs • es' • sət • ēz') *n.* plural form of **necessity:** something that is needed (page 220)

installed (in • stôld') *v.* a form of the verb **install:** to put in place for use or service (page 223)

featuring (fē' • chûr • ing) *adj.* having as the main attraction (page 227)

discount (dis' • kount) *adj.* with lowered prices (page 227)

expire (eks • pīr') *v.* to come to an end (page 228)

Practice

Match each word with its definition.

1. installed — **a.** something special

2. particular — **b.** put in place for use

3. discount — **c.** to come to an end

4. expire — **d.** things that are needed

5. produce — **e.** fresh fruits and vegetables

6. necessities — **f.** having as the main attraction

7. seasonal — **g.** with lowered prices

8. featuring — **h.** ripe at a particular time

Apply **The underlined vocabulary words have gotten mixed up. Cross each word out, and write the correct word beneath each sentence.**

9. Strawberries and raspberries are ~~expire~~ fruits.

   seasonal

10. I don't like most bike shops; I like that ~~featuring~~ bike shop.

    particular

11. Sandy's dad ~~discount~~ a new radio in the car.

    installed

12. Pedro knew he needed to use the coupon because it was about to ~~produce~~. expire

13. The family bought ~~installed~~ at a farmer's market.

    produce

14. Food and water are ~~seasonal~~ of life.

    necessities

15. Everything was less than $1.00 at the ~~necessities~~ store.

    discount

16. The grocery store is ~~particular~~ a special price for oranges.

    featuring

Name ______________________ Date __________

Main Idea and Supporting Details

A main idea helps the reader focus on story events or information. Details provide more information.

- The **main idea** tells you what a story or part of a story is about.
- **Details** or reasons help the reader know more about the main idea. Sometimes these details are *facts,* which can be proven true. Sometimes these details are *opinions,* which tell how a person thinks or feels about something.

Look through "What Ever Happened to the Baxter Place?" for a main-idea sentence that is followed by details or reasons. Write one main idea, and then give some details about it. Possible Answers

Page: 210 Main idea: The Baxter family owned a farm.

Detail about the main idea: It had acres of fields, meadows, and woodlands.

Detail about the main idea: Cows grazed in the east meadow.

Read the following lists of reasons (details). Write a main idea to fit each list.

Possible Answers

1. to have fun

to cool off on a hot day

to splash in the water

to exercise

The main idea: why people go swimming

2. to keep us warm

to shelter us from snow or rain

to have a place to keep our things

to make something beautiful

The main idea: why people build or live in houses

Write three sentences—one main-idea sentence and two detail sentences that support the main idea.

I like school. I get to see my friends at school. I learn new things there, too.

Name ______________________ Date ____________

Writing a Play

Audience: Who will read your play?

Possible Answer classmates who will perform it

Purpose: What is your purpose for writing the play?

Possible Answer I want to tell the story of my great-grandmother's move to America.

Prewriting **Use this organizer to help you plan your play.**

Possible Answers

Characters

Kirsten (my great-grandmother); her mom; Pauline

Props

book (to be an English reader)

Setting

a farmhouse in Minnesota, 1900

Plot

Beginning: Kirsten and her mom arrive at the new farmhouse.

Middle: Kirsten misses Sweden, but makes friends with Pauline, who helps her read and spell English.

End: Kirsten does well at the spelling bee.

Revising

Use this checklist to revise your play.

- ☐ Does your play have well-developed characters and dialogue?
- ☐ Does it have a specific setting?
- ☐ Does the plot have a problem that is solved?
- ☐ Are your stage directions clear?
- ☐ Do the stage directions support what the characters are saying?
- ☐ Does your story happen in an order that makes sense?
- ☐ Could actors on a stage perform your play?

Editing/Proofreading

Use this checklist to correct mistakes.

- ☐ Are the characters' names at the beginning of their lines?
- ☐ Did you use correct spellings?
- ☐ Did you put the stage directions in parentheses?
- ☐ Did you use correct punctuation?

Publishing

Use this checklist to prepare your play for an audience.

- ☐ Give your play a title.
- ☐ Neatly rewrite or type a final copy.
- ☐ Make a sketch of how you will set up your stage.
- ☐ If possible, perform your play with classmates.

Name ______________________ Date __________

Spelling

This lesson reviews words with **prefixes, affixes** that change word meaning, and **word families.**

Sort the spelling words under the correct heading.

Order will vary under heading.

Prefixes

1. mismatch
2. preview
3. bicycle
4. unfair
5. autopilot
6. distrust
7. midsummer
8. indirect

Word family *direct*

9. direct
10. direction
11. indirect
12. director

Word List

1. mismatch
2. preview
3. movement
4. bicycle
5. doubtful
6. restless
7. restful
8. direct
9. direction
10. director
11. indirect
12. autopilot
13. distrust
14. unfair
15. midsummer

Challenge Words

16. misspell
17. knowledge

Spelling (continued)

Affixes that change word meaning

13. movement — mismatch
14. doubtful — preview
15. restful — bicycle
16. restless — unfair
17. autopilot — distrust
18. midsummer — direction
19. indirect — director

Name ______________________ Date __________

Complex Sentences

Focus A **complex sentence** is made of one complete sentence, called an **independent clause,** combined with an incomplete idea, called a **dependent clause.**

I will play on the playground after lunch is over. (*after lunch is over* is a dependent clause)

A dependent clause, or a **subordinate clause,** cannot stand on its own as a sentence.

After lunch is over (does not make sense on its own)

After lunch is over, I will play on the playground. (explains the subordinate clause)

The two parts of a complex sentence are joined by **subordinating conjunctions** such as: *after, although, as, because, before, if, since, when, where, while, until,* and *unless.*

A complex sentence helps a reader know what idea is most important.

Although my friend invited me, I don't want to go.

Circle the subordinating conjunction in each complex sentence below.

1. Because I wanted a sandwich, my mom stopped at the deli.
2. Unless the team practices, they will not win the game.
3. Quinn read the book although it was very difficult.
4. If you want to stay healthy, you should drink plenty of water.

Apply **Read each sentence below. Circle the dependent or subordinate clause.**

5. Before the family sat at the picnic table, rain began to pour.
6. Their games had not been as fun since Tara quit the team.
7. Grandma and Grandpa took a walk after dinner was finished.
8. Because I did not study, I did not pass the test.

Read each pair of sentences below. The writer made a mistake, and left one sentence incomplete. Write a complete complex sentence that includes both ideas. **Possible Answers**

9. Raul would not go to the party. Unless Margarita invited him.

   Unless Margarita invited him, Raul would not go to the party.

10. When she found out. Margarita called Raul.

   When she found out, Margarita called Raul.

11. She said she was sorry. Because she had forgotten to call earlier.

   She said she was sorry because she had forgotten to call earlier.

12. After Margarita called. Raul went to the party.

   After Margarita called, Raul went to the party.

Name ______________________________ Date ____________

Story Map and Character Web

Focus You can use different types of organizers to help you plan a story.

- A **story map** helps you identify the elements of a story.
- A **character web** helps you organize ideas and thoughts about a character.

Practice **Use the character web below to organize ideas about a character.**

Possible Answers

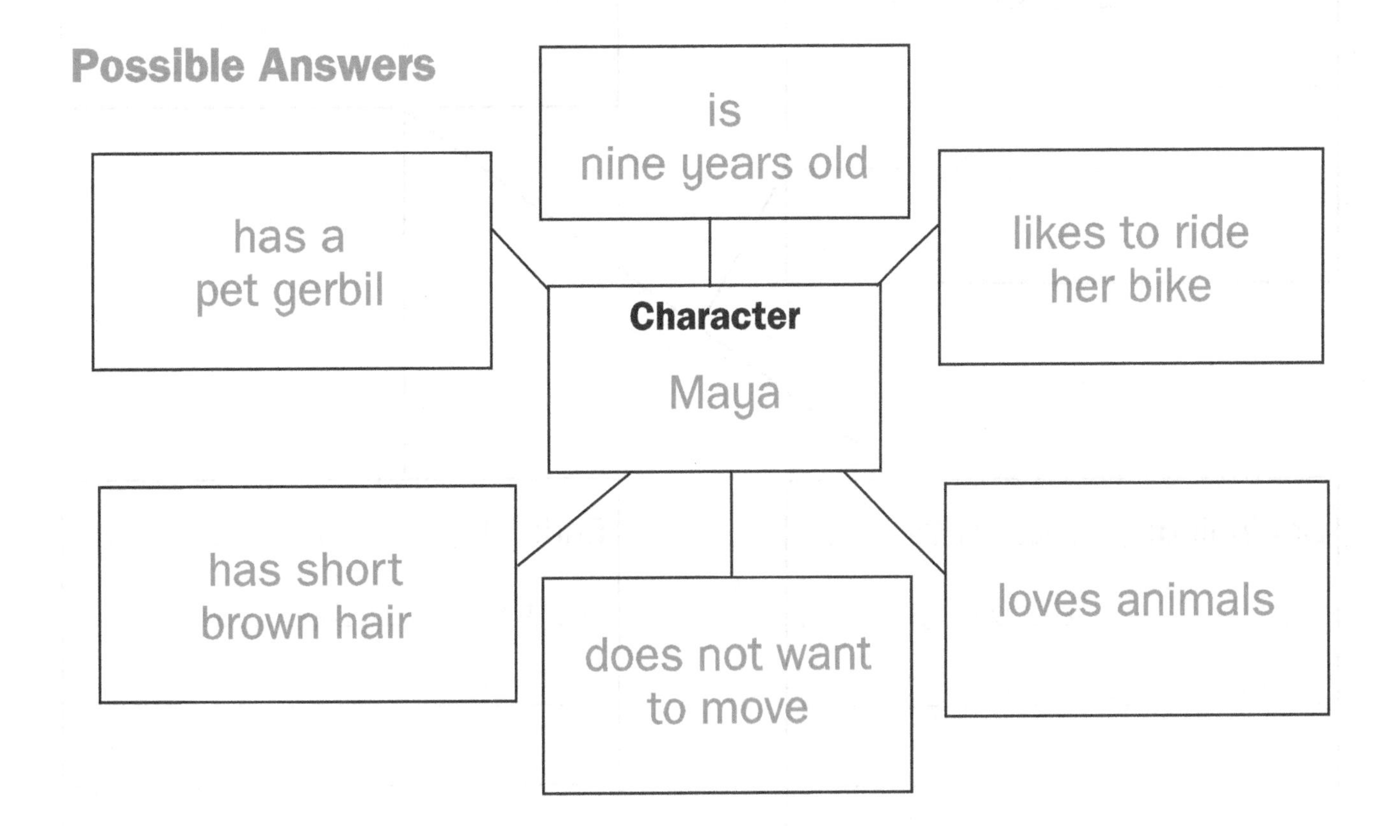

Story Map and Character Web (continued)

Use the story map below to organize ideas for your story.

Possible Answers

Problem to be solved: Maya does not want to move.

Climax: Maya visits the new place and makes a friend. She finally feels hopeful about the move.

Middle: Maya tries to find ways to stop the move.

Beginning: Maya finds out her family is moving to a new state.

End: Maya says good-bye to her old house.

Name _______________ Date _______

Antonyms, Synonyms, and Compound Words

Focus

- **Antonyms** are words that have opposite meanings.

  Loud and *quiet* are antonyms.

- **Synonyms** are words with the same, or nearly the same, meaning.

  Loud and *noisy* are synonyms.

A dictionary or thesaurus can help you find synonyms and antonyms for many words.

Practice A **Read the following sentences from "Tomás and the Library Lady." Answer the questions below.**

Answers will vary.

Papá Grande smiled and said, "More stories for the new storyteller."

1. Look in a thesaurus or a dictionary.
Find two synonyms for the word *smile.* beam grin

2. Find an antonym for the word *smile.* frown

3. If words are synonyms, they should each give a sentence a similar meaning. Could your synonyms replace *smiled* in the story sentence?

yes

Tomás read about tiger eyes shining brightly in the jungle at night.

4. Look up *shining* and *brightly* in a thesaurus.
What are two synonyms for *shining?* gleaming glimmering

5. What is an antonym for *brightly?* Make sure to think about the meaning of *brightly* in this sentence. darkly

Focus

A **compound word** is a single word formed from two words.

Sometimes a compound word has the same meaning as the two words in it. Sometimes it has a new meaning.

bird + **house** = **birdhouse** ("a house for a bird")

cow + **boy** = **cowboy** ("a male who herds cattle")

Practice B

Circle a compound word in each sentence. Write a definition for each word. Use a dictionary if you need help.

6. The storyteller sat down and began to tell a tale.
   a person who tells stories

7. Aisha put her bookmark inside the book before going to bed.
   something to keep your place in a book

8. The hummingbird buzzed from flower to flower.
   a small bird that makes a humming sound

Read the sentence from "Tomás and the Library Lady." Answer the questions.

He had taught the library lady how to say "Good afternoon, sir" in Spanish.

9. What word in this sentence is a compound word? afternoon

10. Write the two words that make up this word. after + noon

11. Look up each of these words in a dictionary. Does this compound word use the meanings of both words? Explain your answer.
    Yes, it does, because afternoon means a time after noon.

Name ______________________ Date __________

Contractions and Related Words

Focus

A **contraction** is a word formed from two or more words. Some letters are left out when the words combine.

- An apostrophe (') marks the spot where the letters were dropped.
- Some contractions look the same, but mean different things.

  Example: *He'd* can mean "he had" or "he would."

Practice A

Write the words that combine to make each contraction. Some contractions can be made by two sets of words.

1. I'd   I + had
   I + would
2. can't   can + not
3. we'd   we + had
   we + would
4. she's   she + is

Read the sentence below. Circle the pair of words that can be made into a contraction. Write the contraction on the line.

5. My sister and I decided we would make cookies.

   we'd

Lesson 1

Focus **Related words** are words with a common theme. They are words that could be found in the same grouping.

Example: The words *nest, eggs,* and *seed* all relate to birds.

Practice B **Read each set of words below. Cross out the word that is not related to the others.**

6. bake oven recipe ~~bed~~ food
7. art ~~sports~~ paintbrush drawing artist
8. ~~actor~~ athlete football Olympics game
9. dog zebra zoo koala ~~flower~~

Read each sentence below. Decide which word from the word bank is in the same word family as the underlined word. Write it on the line.

swing	library	nature	city

10. The group hiked into the dark forest. nature
11. Reading books is one of my favorite activities. library
12. The children climbed the jungle gym on the playground. swing
13. Windows on the tall buildings glowed in the darkness. city

Name ______________________ Date __________

Selection Vocabulary

Focus

gulps (gulps) *n.* plural form of **gulp:** a large amount swallowed at one time (page 248)

cot (kot) *n.* a type of bed (page 249)

howling (houl' • ing) *v.* a form of the verb **howl:** to make a loud, wailing cry (page 250)

lap (lap) *v.* to drink a liquid by lifting it up with the tongue (page 254)

setting (set' • ting) *v.* a form of the verb **set:** to go down below the horizon (page 255)

borrow (bor' • rōw) *v.* to take something from another person with the understanding that it must be given back (page 255)

eager (ē' • gûr) *adj.* wanting very much to do something (page 255)

package (pak' • əj) *n.* a thing or group of things packed, wrapped up, or tied together; a bundle (page 259)

Read each sentence. Write *Yes* if the definition matches the way the underlined word is used. Write *No* if it does not.

1. I was <u>eager</u> to get my new cat.

   the amount swallowed at one time No

2. But she was <u>howling</u> and meowing when I brought her home.

   making a loud, wailing cry Yes

3. I gave her water, and she began to <u>lap</u> it up.

   to drink a liquid by lifting it up with the tongue Yes

Lesson 1

Apply **Use the clues to complete the crossword puzzle below.**

							4 e		
						5 l	a	p	
							g		
	6 g				7 h		e		
	u			8 b	o	r	r	o	w
	l				w				
	p				l				
	9 s	e	t	t	i	n	g		
					n				
10 p	a	11 c	k	a	g	e			
		o							
		t							

Across

5. to drink a liquid by lifting it up with the tongue

8. to take something from another person with the understanding that it must be given back

9. a form of the verb set: to go down below the horizon

10. a bundle

Down

4. wanting very much to do something

6. the amounts swallowed at one time

7. making a loud, wailing cry

11. a type of bed

Name ______________________________ Date ____________

Generating Ideas and Questions about Storytelling

Think about stories in your family. Answers will vary.

What stories about your family do you know? Summarize a story that people in your family tell often.

My family tells about the time when a tree branch fell on top of grandpa's head. Grandpa says that it made him smarter. My uncles say that he is the same. My aunts giggle and say that grandpa is "silly in the head."

Things that you don't know about your family would be fun to investigate.

What are some things that you wonder about your family? What stories would you like to hear or read about your family?

I would like to know how my parents met, why my Uncle Johnny limps, and what school was like for my grandmother in Germany. I can't imagine living in Germany or going to school there. It must have been neat.

Generating Ideas and Questions about Storytelling (continued)

Think about the most interesting stories that you have heard or told. Answers will vary.

What interesting stories do you know? Summarize a really interesting story that someone has told you. My neighbor, Mrs. Radcliffe, tells me every summer about the summer that was so hot that the tree in her front yard caught fire. My sister was born that summer. Mrs. Radcliffe says that my sister used to look out the window and cry when she saw the burnt tree in her yard.

If you were to tell a story, what story would you tell?

I would tell the story of my first week at my new school.

Why would you choose that story?

I got lost my first day of school and walked into the janitor's closet instead of my classroom. Everyone laughed at me. But the next day was better. By the end of my first week, I made four new friends and joined the school band.

Writing a Couplet

Audience: Who will read your couplet?

Possible Answer my classmates

Purpose: What is your reason for writing the couplet?

Possible Answer I want to entertain others with a poem.

Prewriting **Use this graphic organizer to plan your couplet.**

Possible Answers

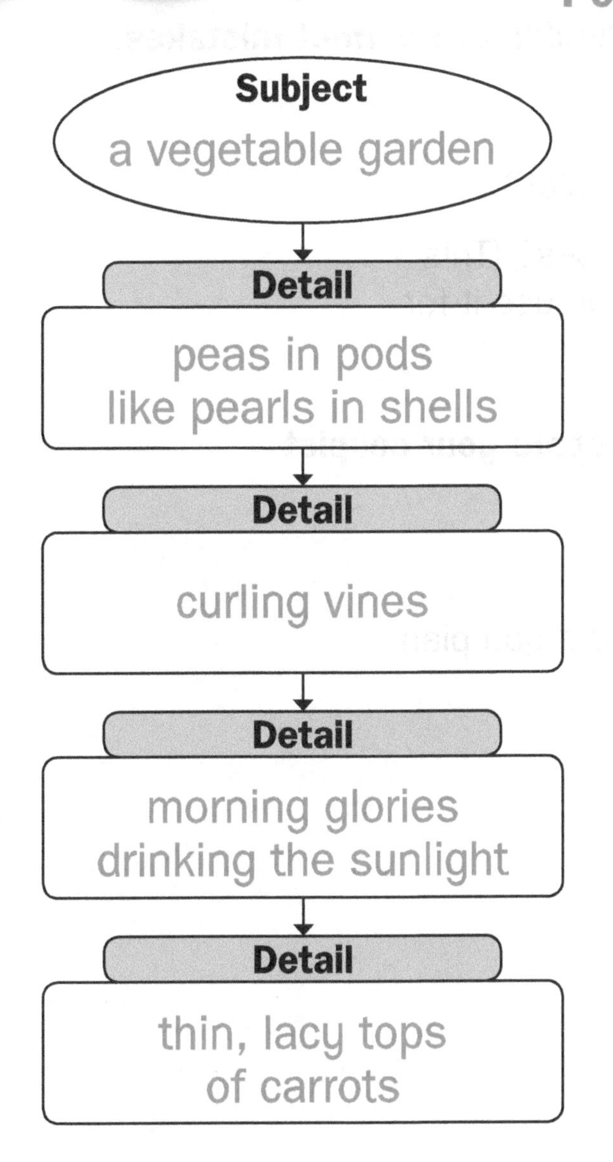

Rhyming Word List

hard	yard
grow	show
stick	pick
tall	fall

Revising

Use this checklist to revise your couplet.

- ☐ Does your poem meet your purpose for writing?
- ☐ Did you put rhyming words at the end of lines?
- ☐ Did you use descriptive words?
- ☐ Do your lines sound smooth?
- ☐ Does your poem create pictures or feelings for a reader?

Editing/Proofreading

Use this checklist to correct mistakes.

- ☐ Did you use correct spelling?
- ☐ Did you capitalize the title of your couplet?
- ☐ Did you use punctuation to make pauses? (This is not necessary in poetry, but you can use it for added effect.)

Publishing

Use this checklist to prepare your couplet for publication.

- ☐ Neatly rewrite or type a final copy.
- ☐ Practice reading your couplet out loud if you plan to give a presentation.

Name ______________________ Date __________

Spelling

Focus This lesson reviews **long vowel** sound/spellings, **/j/, /s/, /n/, /r/, /f/, /m/, consonant blends, compound words, related words,** and **contractions.**

Practice **Sort the spelling words under the correct heading.**

Order will vary under heading.

Contractions

1. didn't
2. you're

/j/ and a consonant blend

3. strange

/s/ or /f/ sound/spellings

4. orphan — scarf
5. concert — strange

Long vowel sounds /ē/, /ā/, /ī/, and /ū/

6. peanut — strange
7. mute

Word List

1. strange
2. concert
3. peanut
4. washcloth
5. mute
6. these
7. wrap
8. didn't
9. pupil
10. limb
11. jacket
12. scarf
13. orphan
14. knuckle
15. you're

Challenge Words

16. eager
17. package
18. wristband

Spelling (continued)

8. these
9. pupil

/m/, /n/, /r/ sound/spellings

10. knuckle
11. limb
12. wrap
13. scarf
14. you're
15. mute
16. strange
17. concert
18. didn't
19. orphan

Compound word

20. washcloth peanut

Related words

21. jacket
22. scarf

Name ______________________ Date __________

Nouns; Verbs and Verb Phrases; Subjects and Predicates; Complete Simple Sentences

Focus

Nouns name a person, place, thing, or idea.

Verbs show the action, condition, or state of being of the subject. There are action verbs, state-of-being verbs, and linking verbs.

A **verb phrase** is a verb with two or more words. The last verb in a verb phrase is the main verb. Helping verbs come before the main verb.

Practice A

Read this story. Write *yes* if the underlined word is a noun. Write *no* if the underlined word is not a noun.

The story yes of the Frog Prince teaches no about honesty. The princess in the story promises a frog yes he can live at the castle. At first, she does not want no to keep her promise. When she gives the frog a kiss, yes he turns into a prince. By keeping her promise, yes she saves the frog prince.

Read each sentence. Circle *Action Verb* if the sentence has an action verb. Circle *Verb Phrase* if the sentence has a verb phrase.

1. The girls danced to the music. (Action Verb) Verb Phrase
2. I dance, too. (Action Verb) Verb Phrase
3. I will go to school someday to become a dancer. Action Verb (Verb Phrase)

Focus

The **subject** names who or what the sentence is about.

A **simple subject** is the main word or words in a sentence, usually a noun or pronoun. A **compound subject** has two or more subjects combined by a conjunction.

A **simple predicate** shows one thing about the subject. The predicate tells what the subject is or does. A **compound predicate** shows two or more things about the same subject. They are connected by a conjunction.

A complete **simple sentence** has one subject and one predicate.

Practice B **Decide if each sentence below has a simple or compound subject. Write *simple* or *compound.***

4. Aesop told a story of an ant and a chrysalis. simple
5. An ant discovered a chrysalis. simple
6. The chrysalis was moving and swaying. simple
7. The ant and the chrysalis became friends. compound

Decide if each sentence below has a simple or compound predicate. Write *simple* or *compound.*

8. The chrysalis did not say anything. simple
9. The ant walked by later and saw an empty chrysalis. compound
10. Overhead, a butterfly was fluttering and flying. compound

Name ______________________________ Date ____________

Time Lines

Focus A **time line** is a graph that shows when things happen over time. Each dot on a time line stands for a single event and a date or time. Events are listed from left to right in the order they happened. The earliest event is at the far left.

Practice **Look at the time line below. Use it to answer the questions.**

The Life of Maya Angelou, Writer and Poet

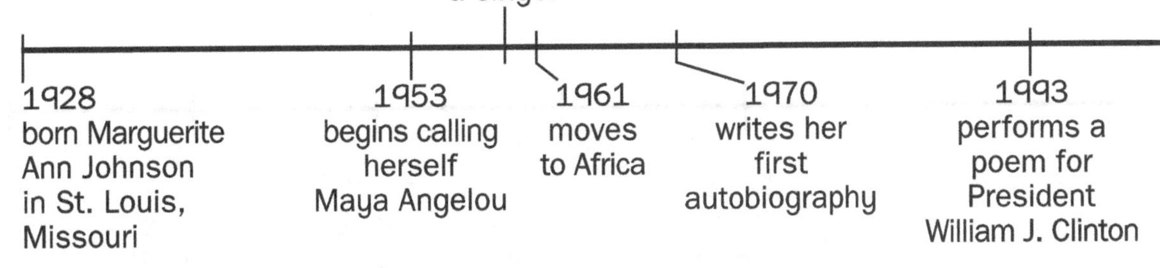

1. What is the subject of this time line?
the life of Maya Angelou

2. When did Maya Angelou change her name?
in 1953

3. Which event happened first: Angelou writes her autobiography, or she works as a singer?
Angelou works as a singer first.

Lesson 1

Reread "Tomás and the Library Lady." Events from the story are listed below. Put them in order on the time line.

Tomás and his family leave Iowa for Texas.

Tomás says goodbye to the library lady.

Tomás meets the library lady.

Tomás and his family leave Texas for Iowa.

Tomás brings Papá Grande to the library.

Tomás goes to the library.

Tomás reads stories to Papá Grande and his parents.

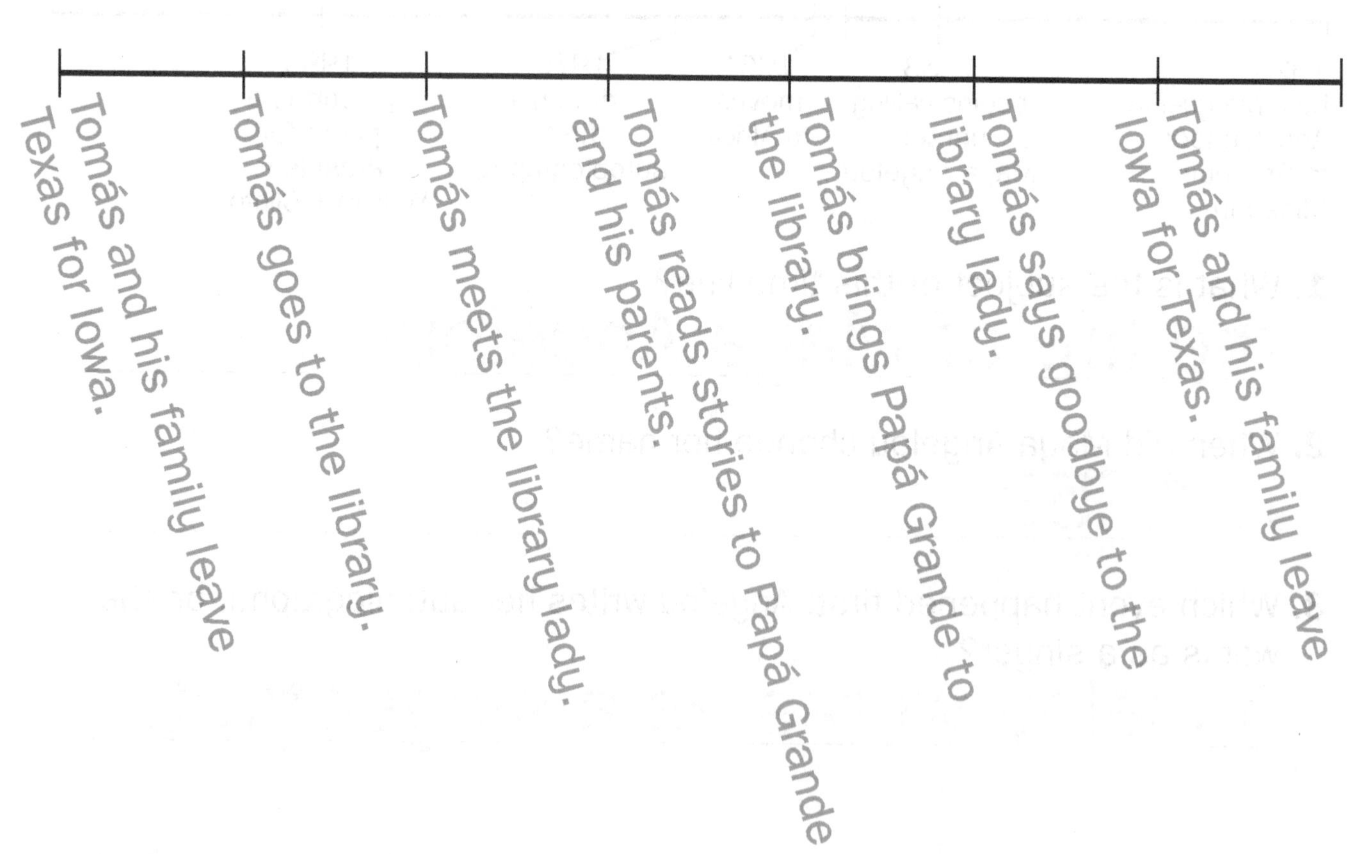

UNIT 6 Lesson 2

Name ____________ Date ________

Regular and Irregular Plural Nouns

Focus To make many words plural, meaning "more than one," add the ending *-s* or *-es.* These types of plurals are called **regular plurals,** because they follow this rule.

The letters *es* are added to words ending in *ch, sh, s, ss, x, z, or zz.* Example: box + es = boxes

When a word ends in a *consonant-y,* change the *y* to *i,* and add *-es.* Example: fly + es = flies

If a word ends in *vowel-y,* just add *-s.*

Example: toy + s = toys

For words that end in *f* or *fe*, change the *f* to *v*, and add *-s* or *-es* to form plurals. Example: wolf – f + ves = wolves

Practice A **Think about how to make each word from the box plural. Sort the plural word into the correct group.**

slide	book	fly	sky	life	horse	bunny	half

Order within groups will vary.

Group 1: Drop *f* added *-ves*

1. halves
2. lives

Group 2: Just added -s

3. books
4. horses
5. slides

Group 3: Changed *y* to *i* and added -es

6. flies
7. bunnies
8. skies

Focus Some plurals do not follow the regular pattern.

- Some words, such as *deer* and *shrimp,* have the same singular and plural forms.
- Some words, such as *goose* and *geese,* change spellings in the plural form.

Example: *tooth, teeth* *man, men*

Practice B **Make each noun plural. Write it on the line. (Remember, some words have the same singular and plural forms.)**

9. one fish several fish
10. one person many people
11. one shrimp a bucket of shrimp
12. one goose a flock of geese
13. one tooth thirty-two teeth
14. one mouse several mice
15. one woman two women

Name ______________________ Date __________

Homophones and Homographs

Focus **Homophones** are words that sound alike but have different spellings and different meanings. Think about the meaning of the word when spelling a homophone.

Example: *Sea* and *see* are homophones.

The words sound alike: sea (sē)   see (sē)

But they have different meanings: *sea* "a large body of salt water"
see "to look at with the eyes"

Practice A **Answer the questions below.**

1. What is the meaning of the underlined word in the sentence below?

   The boy told a new story.

   something that's just been made

2. What is the meaning of the underlined word in the sentence below?

   He knew many old stories too.

   to have been sure

3. Are *new* and *knew* homophones? Why or why not?

   Yes. They sound alike but have different spellings and meanings.

4. Use *new* or *knew* to correctly complete this sentence:

   Consuela was excited to go to a new school.

Focus

Homographs are words that have the same spelling but have different pronunciations and meanings.

Example: *Live* and *live* are homographs.

live (liv) "to make one's home"

live (līv) "living"

You can learn the meanings of homographs and how to pronounce them. Then, when you read one in a sentence, you will understand which word is being used.

Practice B **Read the following sentence, and answer the questions about it.**

The wind was howling in the treetops.

5. Does the letter *i* in *wind* sound like the /i/ sound in *big* or the /ī/ sound in *line*? /i/

6. What is the meaning of the word *wind* in the sentence? moving air

7. Say *wind* with the /ī/ sound. The words *wind* (wind) and *wind* (wīnd) are homographs. Find the definitions for the two words in a dictionary. **Possible Answers**

wind (wind) the natural movement of air

wind (wīnd) to wrap with something flexible

8. Choose one of the meanings above. Use *wind* in a sentence of your own. **Possible Answer** I wind up the kite string.

Name ______________________ Date __________

Selection Vocabulary

Focus

streaming (strēm' • ing) *adj.* running; flowing (page 268)

mantel (man' • təl) *n.* a shelf above a fireplace (page 272)

siren (sī' • rən) *n.* a device that makes a loud, shrill sound (page 272)

scarcely (skârs' • lē) *adv.* barely (page 274)

drenched (drenchd) *v.* past tense of **drench**: to soak completely (page 274)

errand (er' • rənd) *n.* a short trip to do something (page 276)

overcome (o • vûr • cum') *v.* to beat or conquer (page 280)

natural (nach' • ûr • əl) *adj.* found in nature; not made by people (page 281)

Practice **Write the vocabulary word that matches each example below.**

1. a tree natural
2. a shelf above a fireplace mantel
3. a flowing river streaming
4. one team beating another at a game overcome
5. going for a short trip to the store errand
6. a cat in the rain drenched

Lesson 2

Circle the correct vocabulary word to complete each sentence below.

7. Ron, a firefighter, often tells stories of how fires (overcome/natural) houses.
8. He says a smoke detector over a (mantel/drenched), above a door, or in another place in a home can save your life.
9. Once a fire is large, you can see smoke (scarcely/streaming) out over trees and houses.
10. A warning (overcome/siren) rings to tell firefighters about a fire.
11. Sometimes fires start when a person leaves an oven on while running an (errand/mantel).
12. Some fires start because of (natural/streaming) events, such as lightning hitting a tree.
13. Ron has (streaming/drenched) fires with water.
14. Sometimes a house (errand/scarcely) survives a fire.

Name ______________________ Date __________

Generating Ideas and Questions about Storytelling

Think about the reasons people have for telling stories.

List some reasons that someone would want to tell a story.

To remember things that happened. Someone might want to tell a story to make people laugh. Someone might write a story to teach something about people, places, or animals.

What kind of story would you like to tell or write?
How would you want people to react to your story?

I want to write a story about my cat. Because my cat is cute and funny, I would want people to smile and laugh at my story and be nice to cats.

Would you rather tell a story, or write a story? Why?

I want to write a story because people always forget what you tell them.

Generating Ideas and Questions about Storytelling (continued)

Think about what makes a story interesting.

Interesting stories have interesting characters, which may be real people. What people or characters would you like to write about?

a pirate that has two parrots; a girl who is always sick; a dog that talks

An interesting story has a problem that needs to be overcome. List some problems or conflicts that you would like to write about.

a pirate's parrots that are always fighting; not making the soccer team

List some interesting ways to solve or overcome those problems.

get the parrots to talk about what bothers them; practicing all year and trying out next year for the soccer team again

Name ____________________ Date __________

Writing a Quatrain

Audience: Who will read your quatrain?

Possible Answer my classmates

Purpose: What is your reason for writing the quatrain?

Possible Answer I want to explain my feelings in a poem.

Prewriting

Use this graphic organizer to plan your quatrain.

Possible Answers

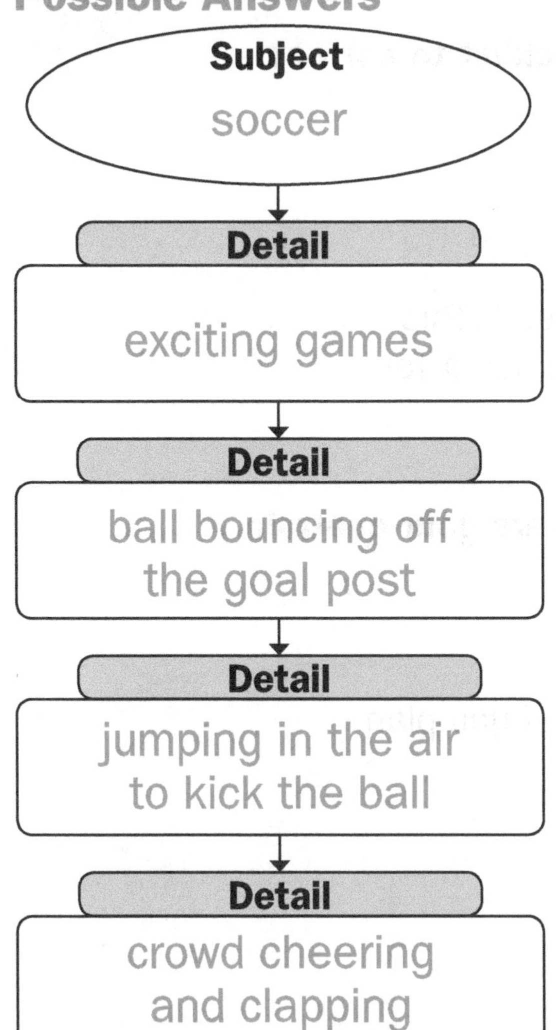

Rhyming Word List

ball	wall
fun	sun
post	most
kick	trick

Revising

Use this checklist to revise your quatrain.

- ☐ Does your poem meet your purpose for writing?
- ☐ Did you put rhyming words at the end of lines?
- ☐ Did you use figurative language, such as similes and metaphors?
- ☐ Did you use sensory adjectives?
- ☐ Do your lines sound smooth?
- ☐ Does your poem create pictures or feelings for a reader?

Editing/Proofreading

Use this checklist to correct mistakes.

- ☐ Did you use correct spelling?
- ☐ Did you capitalize the title of your quatrain?
- ☐ Did you use punctuation to make pauses? (This is not necessary in poetry, but you can use it for added effect.)

Publishing

Use this checklist to prepare your quatrain for publication.

- ☐ Neatly rewrite or type a final copy.
- ☐ Practice reading your quatrain out loud if you plan to give a presentation.

Name ______________________________ Date ____________

Spelling

Focus This lesson reviews homophones, homographs, long vowel sounds, the /o͞o/ sound, *y* to *ies*, and plurals that keep their singular form.

Word List

1. they're
2. there
3. geese
4. moose
5. cue
6. train
7. owner
8. throat
9. steal
10. steel
11. weighty
12. cries
13. bright
14. rubies
15. lead

Challenge Words

1. statue
2. hyena
3. swallow

Practice **Sort the spelling words under the correct heading.**

Homophones

1. they're
2. there
3. steel
4. steal

Plurals where *y* changes to *ies*

5. rubies
6. cries

Irregular plurals

7. geese
8. moose

Spelling (continued)

Words with long vowel sounds

9. train
10. cue
11. owner
12. bright
13. throat
14. weighty
15. steal — steel
16. cries — geese

Homograph:

17. lead

/o͞o/ sound

18. rubies
19. moose

Name ______________________________ Date __________

Punctuation; Possessive Nouns; Plural Nouns

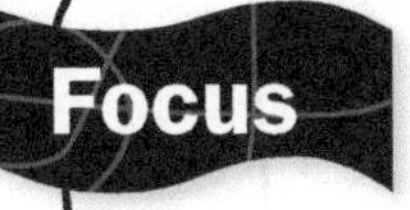

Quotations marks can show when someone is speaking, and they can set off the titles of works such as short stories.

Commas can separate a speaker's words from the rest of a sentence. They can also separate words in a series.

Capitalize the main words of the titles of movies, plays, and television shows. Capitalize the first word of a speaker or a quotation.

Practice A

The writer of the following paragraph made some mistakes using quotation marks, commas, and capitalization. Cross out any incorrect punctuation. Add any missing punctuation.

The Nez Perce tell a story about some large rocks. Long ago, Yellow Jacket and Ant did not get along. One day, Ant saw Yellow Jacket sitting on a rock while eating salmon, vegetables and, other food. "You can't eat there without asking me, Ant said. "I can eat where I like" Yellow Jacket replied. The two started fighting. Coyote came and told them to stop fighting. But they would not stop. "I'm warning you", Coyote said. "stop fighting, or I will turn you to stone." Because they would not stop, Coyote turned them to stone. You can still see them to this day, frozen because of their greed.

Focus A **possessive noun** shows ownership. To make a possessive of

- a single noun, add *'s*.
- a plural noun ending in *s*, add an apostrophe *s'*.
- a plural noun not ending in *s*, add *'s*.

A **possessive pronoun** also shows ownership. It takes the place of a possessive noun.

Plural nouns name more than one person, place, thing, or idea.

For regular nouns

- form the plural by adding -s to singular nouns.
- ending with *s, ch, sh, ss, z, zz,* or *x,* add *-es* to singular nouns.
- ending with a consonant and *y,* change the *y* to *i* and add *-es*.

Some plural nouns are irregular. You must learn their correct spellings.

Practice B **Rewrite each group of words using a possessive noun or pronoun.**

1. the purse belonging to Angela Angela's purse
2. the hair belonging to her her hair
3. the pen belonging to him his pen
4. the lids belonging to the dishes the dishes' lids

Circle the correct plural from each pair of words.

5. My mom tells **storys/stories** of when she was young.
6. When she was three, she had two pet **mousse/mice**.

Name ______________________ Date __________

Review of Tables, Charts, and Graphs; Review of Reading and Interpreting Information

Information can sometimes be presented in **charts, tables, and graphs.** They show a lot of information in a small space.

Look at the table below. Use it to answer the questions.

Third Grade Classes' Favorite Stories

Class Teacher	Favorite Poem	Favorite Fairytale	Favorite Book
Ms. Adams	"Sick" by Shel Silverstien	"Rapunzel"	*James and the Giant Peach* by Roald Dahl
Mr. Keim	"Last Night I Dreamed of Chickens" by Jack Prelutsky	"Jack and the Beanstalk"	*Charlotte's Web* by E. B. White

1. What is the title of the chart?

Third Grade Classes' Favorite Stories

2. What is Mr. Keim's class's favorite fairytale?

"Jack and the Beanstalk"

3. What is Ms. Adams's class's favorite poem?

"Sick"

Apply **Look at the following graph. Answer the questions below.**

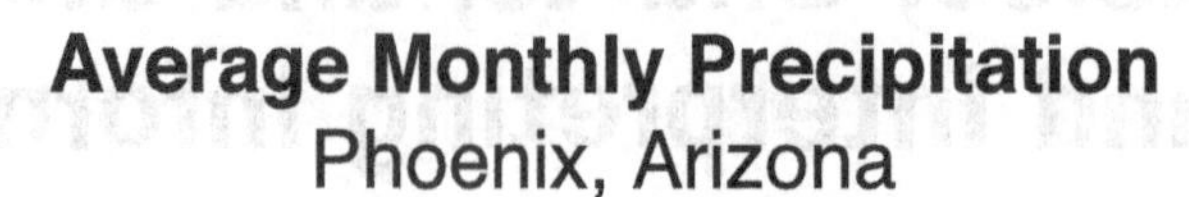

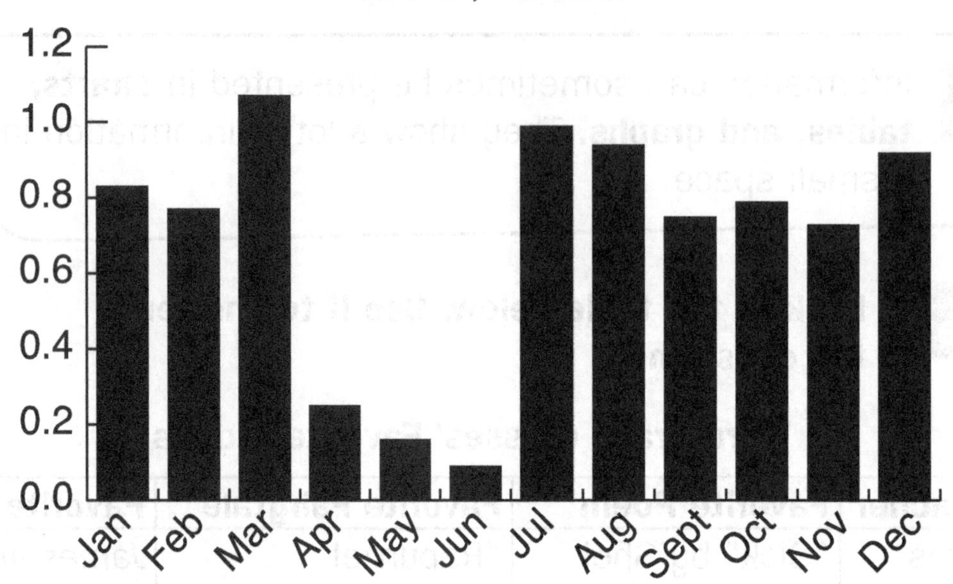

4. When does Phoenix usually get the most rainfall? March

5. If you used this graph, could you know for sure how much rain Phoenix will get next March? Why or why not?

No, it could be an unusual month.

6. A certain plant needs at least 0.8 inches of water per month. Use the chart to interpret whether that would be a good outdoor plant in Phoenix. Explain your answer.

No, seven months of the year Phoenix gets less than 0.8 inches.

7. Could you interpret how hot Phoenix is by using this chart? Explain your answer.

No, it only shows how much rain Phoenix gets.

Name ______________________ Date __________

Inflectional Endings *-ed* and *-ing*

Focus Adding ***-ed*** to a verb makes the action *past tense.* For words that end

- in a vowel and consonant, double the final consonant before adding *-ed.*

  Example: clap ⟶ clapped
- with a silent *e,* drop the e before adding *-ed.*

  Example: tape ⟶ taped
- in *consonant-y,* change the *y* to *i* before adding *-ed.*

  Example: study ⟶ studied

Practice A **Read each sentence. Write *Yes* if *-ed* was used correctly. Write *No* if it was not.**

1. A Tlingit story tells of a man who lived alone. Yes
2. Some bears grabed him. No
3. He promisd them he would give them a feast. No
4. The bears agreed to let him go. Yes
5. He paintted red stripes on his body. No
6. People talked and said the bears would eat him. Yes

Inflectional Endings *-ed* and *-ing*

Focus Adding ***-ing*** to a word makes it present tense, or something that is happening right now.

- For words that end in the /a/, /e/, /i/, /o/, or /u/ sounds and a consonant, double the final consonant before adding *-ing*. *clap* ⟶ *clapping*
- For words that end with a silent *e*, drop the *e* before adding *-ing*. *tape* ⟶ *taping*
- For words ending in a consonant or *y*, add *-ing*.

draw ⟶ *drawing* *study* ⟶ *studying*

Practice B **The writer of these sentences forgot to use *-ing*. Rewrite each underlined word, correctly adding *-ing*.**

7. The plants in my garden are grow. growing
8. The tomatoes are climb the tomato poles. climbing
9. When I am stake the tomatoes, I retie the plants to the stakes. staking
10. I like dig out weeds. digging
11. The basil leaves are reach toward the sun. reaching
12. Water the plants is important. Watering

Name ______________________________ Date ____________

Comparative and Superlative Adjectives

Focus

- **Comparative** adjectives compare two nouns. Add *-er* to most short adjectives to make them comparative.
  Use the word *more* before some longer adjectives.
- **Superlative** adjectives compare three or more nouns. Add *-est* to most short adjectives to make them superlative. Use the word *most* before some longer adjectives.

Practice A **Circle the correct comparative adjective in each sentence.**

1. The train is (faster/more fast) than the car.
2. The track is (smoother/more smooth) now that they fixed it.
3. Gas was (expensiver/more expensive) than a train ticket.

Circle the correct superlative adjective in each sentence.

4. It had the (smallest/most small) print I've ever seen.
5. The story was the (most excitingest/most exciting) I've read.
6. It is the (longest/most longest) book on my shelf.

Focus Some comparative and superlative adjectives are **irregular.** This means they do not follow the rules.

- Irregular comparative and superlative adjectives do not add *-er* or *-est.*

Adjective		**Comparative**		**Superlative**
good	→	better	→	best

- They change spellings.

The pond had little water.

The bucket had less water.

Practice **Choose a comparative or superlative adjective from the box to complete each sentence.**

farther	**worse**	**more**
better	**worst**	**farthest**

7. The worst cold I ever had was last winter.

8. My dad had a bad cold too, but my cold was worse.

9. It took me a long time to feel better.

10. I was out hiking and had to walk farther than I wanted to.

11. That three miles was the farthest I've ever walked.

12. On that hike, I drank more water than my dad.

Name ______________________ Date __________

Selection Vocabulary

Focus

pueblo (po͞o • e' • blō) *n.* a Native American village consisting of adobe and stone houses joined together (page 290)

modern (mod' • ûrn) *adj.* from the present or recent time (page 290)

traditions (trəd • ish' • ənz) *n.* plural form of **tradition:** the practice of passing down customs, beliefs, or other knowledge from parents to their children (page 290)

ancestors (an' • ses • tûrz') *n.* plural form of **ancestor:** an older family member from long ago (page 291)

pure (pūr) *adj.* not mixed with anything else (page 292)

cylinder (sil' • in • dûr) *n.* a solid or hollow object shaped like a drum or a soup can (page 294)

modeling (mod' • əl • ing) *n.* the making or designing of something (page 298)

concentrate (kon' • sən • trāt) *v.* to give careful attention (page 300)

Practice **Write each word next to its synonym below.**

1. designing modeling
2. recent modern
3. focus concentrate
4. customs traditions
5. unmixed pure
6. relatives ancestors

Apply **Circle the correct vocabulary word to complete each sentence.**

7. If you visit the Navajo National Monument, you can see an old (traditions/pueblo) village.

8. The ancient people who built it did not have (traditions/modern) tools.

9. Artists have drawn pictures (modeling/concentrate) what the village once looked like.

10. When you visit, you ought to (concentrate/pure) and imagine the past.

11. You can see a clay (cylinder/pueblo) used to store water.

12. You can touch the (pure/traditions) sandstone walls.

13. The Hopi believe the builders of this village were their (pure/ancestors).

14. You can learn about the culture and (cylinder/traditions) of the Hopi by studying their drawings and hearing their stories.

Name ______________________ Date __________

Drawing Conclusions

Focus

Writers put information in a story or article to help readers know more about characters or events.

Readers should think about what happened in a story or article and why it happened.

Readers use these clues to **draw conclusions** about a character or event in a story or about information in an article. A conclusion must be supported by the text.

Practice

Reread "Pueblo Storyteller." Write a conclusion you can make about the job of a Cochiti potter. Tell what information you used to reach that conclusion.

Conclusion:

Possible Answer The potter has to work hard to make traditional pots.

Information you used:

Possible Answer The writer's grandfather sometimes crawls through a tunnel to get clay. He then has to knead and mix it.

Apply **Read this paragraph, and draw a line under the best conclusion based on information in the paragraph.**

1. Alo was always eager to go to Hok'ee's house. He tagged along behind Hok'ee wherever he went. He laughed at the things Hok'ee did. Alo always looked forward to going to Hok'ee's house.

   Alo was a pest.
   Alo could not play by himself.
   Alo really liked Hok'ee.

Read these paragraphs. Write one conclusion for each.

2. The boys had chosen the tree they would use as soon as they moved into their new house. They found old, sturdy wood to use for the floor. They saved their money to buy nails. After working from morning until supper for many days, the boys finished their project.

   Possible Answer The boys were building a tree house.

3. Two new boys moved in next door to Janie. Janie watched the boys every day. One day, she asked if she could help the boys, but they said no. Janie was disappointed. She was hoping that she could make friends with the new boys and that they could help her care for a bird's nest she found.

   Possible Answer The boys do not want to be friends with Janie.

Name ______________________ Date ________

Making a Conjecture

Our group's research question is:

How do you write a good mystery story?

These are some things we already know about our topic or question:

You have to make the reader think. You can't tell the reader too much. The easy answer to the mystery has to be wrong.

Based on what we already know about our topic or question, this is our conjecture:

A good mystery story has a problem that is hard to figure out, and it surprises the reader.

Identifying Needs and Making Plans

Our investigation question is:

Why do people write fictional stories instead of true ones?

These are things our group still needs to know about our investigation topic:

Why do so many stories have talking animals? How is fiction useful? Why do people read fiction if it's not real? What makes good fiction?

List here people or places that you could get the information you need from:

We can ask authors who write fiction and people who read fiction. We can also read more books and articles about fiction.

Use these ideas about who or where to get information from to find information sources for your investigation.

Name ______________________ Date __________

Writing a Limerick

Audience: Who will read your limerick?

Possible Answer my classmates

Purpose: What is your reason for writing the limerick?

Possible Answer I want to make people laugh.

Prewriting

Use this graphic organizer to plan your limerick.

Possible Answers

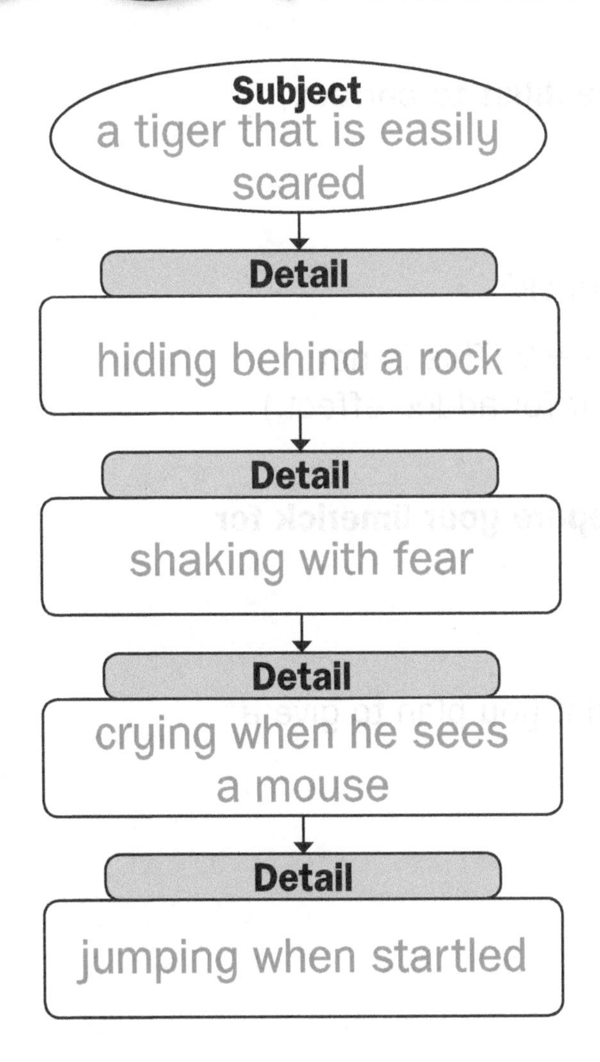

Rhyming Word List

near	fear
by	cry
hear	clear
shake	quake

Revising

Use this checklist to revise your limerick.

- ☐ Does your limerick meet your purpose for writing?
- ☐ Will your limerick make a reader laugh?
- ☐ Did you put rhyming words at the end of lines?
- ☐ Did you follow the rhyme and rhythm patterns of a limerick?
- ☐ Did you use figurative language, such as similes and metaphors?
- ☐ Did you use sensory adjectives?
- ☐ Do your lines sound smooth?

Editing/Proofreading

Use this checklist to correct mistakes.

- ☐ Did you use correct spelling?
- ☐ Did you capitalize the title of your limerick?
- ☐ Did you use punctuation to make pauses? (This is not necessary in poetry, but you can use it for added effect.)

Publishing

Use this checklist to prepare your limerick for publication.

- ☐ Neatly rewrite or type a final copy.
- ☐ Practice reading your limerick out loud if you plan to give a presentation.

Name ______________________ Date __________

Spelling

Focus This lesson reviews the **/oo/ sound spelled *oo*, the /o͞o/ spelled oo, the /aw/ sound, the /ow/ sound, the /oi/ sound, comparative** and **superlative adjectives.**

Word List

1. foot
2. prowl
3. bounce
4. walk
5. thought
6. departing
7. more
8. cuter
9. stall
10. soon
11. stumbled
12. hoist
13. greatest
14. pure
15. vault

Challenge Words

16. uniform
17. haughty

Practice **Sort the spelling words under the correct heading.**

Words with the /aw/ sound

1. walk
2. thought
3. stall
4. vault

Comparative or superlative adjective

5. more
6. cuter
7. greatest

Word with the /oo/ sound

8. foot

Word with the /o͞o/ sound

9. soon

Word with the /oi/ sound

10. hoist

Words with the /ow/ sound

11. prowl

12. bounce

Inflectional endings *-ing* or *-ed*

13. departing

14. stumbled

Selection Vocabulary word

15. pure

Name ______________________ Date ____________

Types of Sentences, and Pronouns

Focus A sentence is a group of words that makes a complete thought about something.

Declarative sentences provide information. They end with a period. **Interrogative** sentences ask questions. They end with a question mark. **Exclamatory** sentences show strong emotion. They end with an exclamation point. **Imperative** sentences give commands or make requests. They end with a period.

Practice A

Identify each sentence as declarative, interrogative, exclamatory, or imperative.

1. Many countries around the world tell stories like "Cinderella." declarative
2. This story tells the Spice Islands story of Demura, a girl like Cinderella. declarative
3. "Wash my dress, Demura." imperative
4. Wouldn't you have been sad too? interrogative
5. The crocodile asks her to rock its baby in a cradle! exclamatory

UNIT 6

Lesson 3

Remember that a **subject** is who or what a sentence is about. A **direct object** receives the action of the subject.

A noun can be the **subject** of a sentence.

The dog ate.

A noun can also be the **direct object** of a sentence.

The dog ate the food.

A **pronoun** can replace the object noun in a sentence.

The dog ate it. (*It* replaces the object noun *food*)

Practice B **Draw a line under the subject noun and circle the direct object noun in each sentence.**

6. Demura rocks the baby crocodile.
7. The crocodile hands a lovely sarong to Demura.
8. But Demura's stepmother and stepsister take the sarong.
9. Then her stepsister copies Demura.

Cross out the direct object noun in the second sentence. Replace it with the correct pronoun.

10. Her stepsister rocks the baby crocodile. But her stepsister mistreats the ~~baby crocodile~~ it.

Name ______________________ Date __________

Schedule

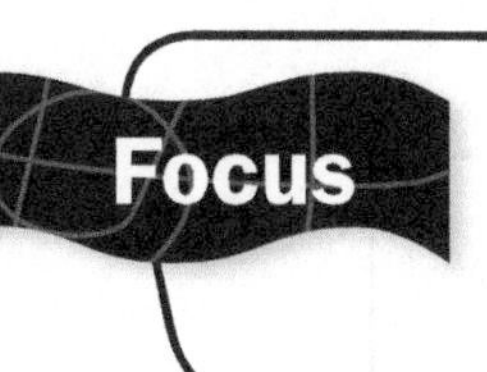

A **schedule** is a plan. It shows what you will do and when you will do it. It can also help you remember all the steps in a job. It reminds you of what you need to do next.

A girl named Hideko made the following schedule. Read it, and answer the questions below.

7:00	Wake up	**7:45**	Take shower
7:05	Make bed	**8:00**	Dry hair and get dressed
7:15	Pack lunch	**8:15**	Walk to bus stop
7:30	Eat breakfast		

1. What title would you give this schedule?

   Possible Answer Weekday Morning Schedule

2. What does Hideko do right after she eats breakfast?

   She takes a shower.

3. How much total time does Hideko take to get ready?

   1 hour and 15 minutes

4. Why do you think Hideko might have made this schedule?

   Possible Answer She had trouble getting ready in time for school.

Lesson 3

Apply **Reread "Pueblo Storyteller." The schedule below shows the steps April's grandmother and grandfather take when making pottery. But some of the steps are missing. Write each missing step from the box in its proper place.**

Soak clay in water.	Fire the pottery.
Paint it with slip.	Attach children to storyteller.
Sift sand.	

Day 1

1. Drive to Mesa to get clay.

2. Soak clay in water.

Day 2

1. Collect white sand.

2. Sift sand.

3. Work sand into the clay.

Day 3

1. Make a clay slab.

2. Shape it into children figures.

Days 4–6

Let pottery dry.

Day 7

1. Sand pottery.

2. Paint it with slip.

3. Let dry.

Day 8

1. Polish and paint the pottery.

2. Let dry.

Day 9

1. Build a kiln.

2. Fire the pottery.

3. Attach children to storyteller.

Name ______________________ Date __________

Suffixes *-ly, -y, -ment, -tion, -ful,* and *-able*

Focus

The suffix ***-ly*** can be added to some adjectives.

If the base word ends in *y*, change the *y* to *i* before adding *-ly*. *happy* ⟶ *happily*

The suffix ***-y*** can be added to some nouns.

Drop a final e before adding *-y*. *shade* ⟶ *shady*

You usually double a consonant before *-y*. *fun* ⟶ *funny*

The suffix ***-ment*** can be added to some verbs. It means "action" or "process."

Practice A **Read each sentence below. Complete the definition of the underlined word.**

Possible Answers

1. The boys finally came to an agreement.

   Agreement means "the action of agreeing."

2. Anna gently touched the starfish.

   Gently means "in a gentle way."

3. Everyone covered his ears when the noisy train went by.

   Noisy means "full of noise."

4. She shook her head sadly.

   Sadly means "in a sad way."

Focus The suffix ***-tion*** can be added to some verbs. It also means "action" or "process."

Drop a final *e* before adding *-tion.* Do not double the letter *t.*
celebrate ⟶ celebration

The suffix ***-ful*** can be added to some nouns. This suffix means "full of."

If the base word ends in *y,* change the *y* to *i* before adding *-ful.*
beauty ⟶ beautiful

The suffix ***-able*** can be added to verbs or nouns. This suffix means "able or tending to be."

For most base words ending in *e,* drop the *e* before adding *-able.* adore ⟶ adorable

Practice B **Correctly add *-tion, -ful,* or *-able* to each base word in the box to complete the sentence.**

5. relate — My ancestor was my relation.
6. educate — You get an education at school.
7. power — The powerful truck pulled the heavy trailer.
8. duty — The dutiful student studied for the test.
9. use — The broken mirror was not usable.
10. read — The clear, careful writing was quite readable.

Name ____________________ Date __________

Suffixes *-ity, -less, -ness,* and *-sion;* Greek and Latin roots

Focus The suffixes ***-ity*** and ***-ness*** can be added to some adjectives. The suffixes mean "state of being."

rare – e + ity = rarity   *happy – y + i + ness = happiness*

The suffix ***-less*** can be added to some nouns. The suffix means "without" or "not having."   *seed + less = seedless*

The suffix ***-sion*** can be added to some verbs. The suffix means "the action of" something.   *decide – de + sion = decision*

Practice A **Use a word to complete each sentence below.**

useless	**discussion**
reality	**kindness**

1. In my dream, I had a discussion with a bird.
2. His wings were broken. They were useless.
3. I showed him kindness and helped him repair his wings.
4. In reality birds do not talk.

Lesson 4

Focus

Greek and **Latin roots** are word parts that have certain meanings.

- ***ast*** means "star." (astronaut)
- ***graph*** means "something written or drawn." (autograph)
- ***log*** (sometimes spelled *logue*) means "to speak." (dialogue)
- ***scop*** means "to look at or examine." (telescope)
- ***grat*** means "thankful or pleasing." (grateful)
- ***mar*** means "sea or ocean." (marine)
- ***miss*** (sometimes spelled *mit*) means "sent." (mission)
- ***port*** means "carry." (portable)

Practice B

Think about the root in each word below. Match each word with its definition.

5. marine
6. autograph
7. congratulate
8. microscope
9. transport
10. mission
11. monologue
12. asterisk

a. to tell people you are happy for them
b. a star-shaped symbol
c. to carry something from one place to another
d. relating to the sea
e. a special job a person is sent to finish
f. a person's handwritten name
g. a speech in a play that is spoken by one person
h. a tool used to look at small things

Name ______________________ Date __________

Selection Vocabulary

Focus

stored (stord) *v.* past tense of **store:** to put away for future use (page 311)

cleared (klērd) *v.* past tense of **clear:** to remove things from (page 311)

survived (sûr • vīvd) *v.* past tense of **survive:** to stay alive (page 312)

boasted (bōst' • əd) *v.* past tense of **boast:** to brag (page 313)

exhausted (egz • ôst' • əd) *adj.* very weak or tired (page 313)

affectionately (əf • fek' • shən • ət • lē') *adv.* with love (page 314)

exaggerated (egz • aj' • jûr • āt' • əd) *v.* past tense of **exaggerate:** to go beyond the truth (page 316)

claim (klām) *v.* to say that something is true (page 319)

Practice **Write *Yes* if the use of the vocabulary word matches the definition below the sentence. Write *No* if it does not.**

1. The mother hugged her child affectionately.

   with love Yes

2. The exhausted dog flopped down on the ground.

   to say something is true No

3. In the past, people stored vegetables in cool basements during winter.

   stayed alive No

4. I cleared out my desk at the end of the year.

put away for future use No

5. All the baby rabbits survived the cold winter.

stayed alive Yes

6. The boy boasted that he could run faster than anyone.

bragged Yes

Circle the vocabulary word that completes each sentence.

7. For many years, people have (survived/affectionately) told tall tales of Paul Bunyan.

8. They (claim/stored) that, because he was so big, the lakes in Minnesota are his footprints.

9. Paul Bunyan (boasted/affectionately) about his strength.

10. He was so big that he (cleared/survived) many forests in one day.

11. He never became (exhausted/boasted) or discouraged.

12. Bunyan and his blue ox, Babe, (exhausted/survived) many dangers.

13. When Bunyan (stored/boasted) some rocks in a pile, he made Mount Hood.

14. People (exaggerated/boasted) tales about a real lumberjack and created this interesting character.

Name ______________________ Date __________

Author's Point of View

Focus Every story is told from a specific **point of view.**

- When a story is told through the eyes of a character, the story is told in the **first-person point of view.** The pronouns *I, me, my, we, us,* and *ours* are used.
- When a story is told directly by the author, the story is told in the **third-person point of view.** The clue words *she, he, her, him,* and *they* are used.

Practice **Look through "Johnny Appleseed" for an example of a sentence that shows point of view. Write it below. Then, answer the questions.** Possible Answers

1. Page: 311

Sentence: As soon as John was old enough to leave home, he set out to explore the vast wilderness to the west.

2. From what point of view is the story told? third-person

3. How did you decide from what point of view the story is told?

by deciding if the author is telling the story directly and by looking for clue words

Apply **Read the paragraph that follows. Decide if it is written in the first-person or third-person point of view. Explain your answer.**

The alarm clock sounded harshly. Tom rubbed his eyes and slowly sat up. Then, he remembered. Today was a special day. He was going with his uncle and cousin for a whole day of hiking in the backcountry. His uncle was going to teach him how to identify trees and other interesting things like that. They might even stay out until dark and learn about some of the stars in the autumn sky. Tom jumped out of bed and put on his hiking clothes.

4. What is the point of view of the paragraph?

third-person

5. How do you know the point of view?

by deciding if the story is told through the eyes of a character or directly by the author and by looking for clue words

Rewrite the paragraph above from another point of view.

Possible Answer The alarm clock sounded harshly. I rubbed my eyes and slowly sat up. Then, I remembered. Today was a special day. I was going with my uncle and cousin for a whole day of hiking in the backcountry. My uncle was going to teach me how to identify trees and other interesting things like that. We might even stay out until dark and learn about some of the stars in the autumn sky. I jumped out of bed and put on my hiking clothes.

Name ______________________ Date ________

Collecting Information

Use these pages to write down good questions to ask a storyteller or an author about your group's particular topic.

Write down the types of stories your group is researching here.

Adventure and Pirate stories

Write out questions you can ask that will give you useful information about the kinds of stories your group is researching. Write out answers you get from authors or storytellers.

Question 1: What's the best pirate story you know and why is it the best?

Answer: *Treasure Island* because of the characters and the treasure hunt.

Question 2: What makes a good pirate character?

Answer: A pirate has to be smart and like gold, but not too mean or people won't cheer for him.

Question 3: Can you tell us about any true pirate stories?

Answer: Blackbeard was a real pirate. His real name was Edward Teach. He was born in England.

Collecting Information

Question 4: What were real pirates like?

Answer: Real pirates were ship captains. Real pirates worked for themselves not for a trading company.

Question 5: How should a good pirate story begin?

Answer: A good pirate story should begin with a pirate ship coming into a port.

Question 6: If you wrote a pirate story, what would it be about?

Answer: I would write a story about a good pirate who loses his ship and tries to get it back.

Writing a Book Review

Audience: Who will read your book review?

Possible Answer my friends

Purpose: What is your reason for writing the book review?

Possible Answer I want to tell people why they should read this book.

Prewriting **Use this graphic organizer to take notes for your book review.**

Possible Answers

Story Map

Title
Paul Bunyan

Main Characters
Paul Bunyan, Babe, other lumberjacks

Plot

Beginning (Problem):
Paul Bunyan is too big, and he has no friends.

Middle (Events):
Paul meets Babe, and they travel together.

Ending (How the Problem Was Solved):
Paul is no longer lonely, because he has Babe.

Opinion:
I liked the book.

Reasons and Details: It was a good story. There were lots of funny moments. The pictures were interesting.

Revising

Use this checklist to revise your book review.

☐ Do you use reasons and details to support your opinion?

☐ Do you tell the plot's main idea in the first sentence?

☐ Are your words clear and specific?

☐ Does your review sound as though you liked or disliked the book?

Editing/Proofreading

Use this checklist to correct mistakes.

☐ Did you indent your paragraphs?

☐ Did you use correct spelling?

☐ Did you capitalize the title of your book or article?

☐ Is the book title underlined?

☐ Did you use correct punctuation for quotations?

Publishing

Use this checklist to prepare your book review for publication.

☐ Neatly rewrite or type a final copy.

☐ Add a drawing or computer graphic.

Name ______________________ Date __________

Spelling

Focus The suffixes ***-ly, -ment, -ful, -able, -less, -ness,*** and ***-sion*** can be added to the end of a word to change the meaning of the word.

When the **inflectional ending *-ing*** is added to a base verb it shows that the action is happening now. **Inflectional ending *-ed*** shows that the action happened in the past.

Some words are derived from **Latin** and **Greek roots.**

Word List

1. astronomer
2. support
3. graphic
4. flawless
5. congratulate
6. quality
7. geologist
8. neatly
9. basement
10. shyness
11. invasion
12. padded
13. painting
14. bendable
15. colorful

Challenge Words

16. affectionately
17. exaggerated
18. exhausted

Sort the spelling words under the correct heading.

Order will vary under heading.

Suffixes *-less* or *-ness*

1. flawless
2. shyness

Inflectional endings *-ed* or *-ing*

3. padded
4. painting

Dropped *de* added *-sion*

5. invasion

Spelling (continued)

Suffixes *-ly, -ment, -ful,* or *-able*

6. neatly
7. basement
8. colorful
9. bendable

Latin roots *grat* and *port*

10. congratulate
11. support

Greek roots *ast, log,* and *graph*

12. astronomer
13. geologist
14. graphic

Remaining adjective

15. quality

Name ______________________________ Date __________

Combining Sentences; Adjectives; Compound Subject and Predicate; Comma Usage

- A **compound** sentence uses a conjunction to combine two simple sentences.
- A simple subject is the main word or words in a sentence. A **compound subject** has two or more simple subjects combined by a conjunction.
- A simple predicate shows one thing about the subject. A **compound predicate** shows two or more things about the same subject. They are connected by a conjunction.

Circle whether each sentence below has a compound subject, a compound predicate, or is a compound sentence.

1. On Saturday, Kelly danced and sang.

compound subject **compound predicate** **compound sentence**

2. The festival began on Friday, and it finished on Sunday.

compound subject **compound predicate** **compound sentence**

3. The musicians and actors performed.

compound subject **compound predicate** **compound sentence**

4. Kelly enjoyed the festival, but he was tired after the long day.

compound subject **compound predicate** **compound sentence**

Focus

- An **adjective** describes a noun or pronoun, telling what kind, how many, or which one. **Comparative** adjectives compare two nouns. **Superlative** adjectives compare three or more nouns.
- Use commas to separate three or more items in a **series.** Use a comma after *yes* and *no* at the beginning of a sentence.

Practice B **The writer of the story below made some mistakes using commas and using comparative and superlative adjectives. Cross out any mistakes, and correct them. Add missing commas.**

One day, Anansi decided to take some food from the chief's farm. Anansi sneaked to the farm. He filled a bag with the ~~most~~ largest hazelnuts, walnuts, and almonds. No, he didn't get caught!

Anansi kept going back. One night, one of the chief's servants saw him. "This is the ~~worsest~~ worst thief," the servant said. "Yes, I've got to catch him."

The servant made the shape of a man out of the ~~most~~ stickiest rubber. He put it near the ~~beautifulest~~ most beautiful hazelnut, walnut, and almond trees. When Anansi saw the rubber man in the darkness, he thought, "Yes, it is alive!" Anansi yelled, screamed, and shouted at the man, but the man didn't move. Anansi grew very mad, and he kicked the man. His foot stuck! He was caught!

Name ______________________ Date __________

Bibliography

A **bibliography** goes at the end of a report and lists the sources you used for the report's information. There is a certain way to list information in your bibliography.

Read the bibliography below. Answer the questions.

Dog Tricks. 2 Jan. 2006. Dog Tricks and Tips. 1 Feb. 2007 <http://www.dogtricksandtips.com/tricks/>.

Swenson, Joy. "How to Teach Your Dog Tricks." Dog Magazine. Mar. 2003: 10–13.

Tellers, Quinn. Training Dogs. New York: Book Publishers, 2001.

1. Where does the first source come from?
   Web site
2. What do you notice about the order of the entries?
   They are in alphabetical order.
3. What do you think the report is going to be about?
   dog tricks
4. When was the issue of Dog Magazine published?
   March 2003

Apply **Using the student's notes below, write a bibliography.**

Notes on book: The title is *Johnny Appleseed.* The author is May Williams. It was published in New York by Skylight Books in 2001.

Notes on magazine: The magazine I used was *History Times.* The article was the January, 2006, issue of "Tall Tales from America." It was written by Paul Cook. It was on pages 18 through 20.

Cook, Paul. "Tall Tales from America." History Times.
Jan. 2006: 18–20.

Williams, May. Johnny Appleseed. New York:
Skylight Books, 2001.

Choose a source you are using for your unit investigation. Write a bibliography entry for that source on the lines below.

Possible Answer "Sioux, Culture." Encyclopedia Britannica.
Chicago: Encyclopedia Britannica, Inc., 2006.

Name ______________________ Date __________

Prefixes *re-*, *un-*, *pre-*, *mis-*, *bi-*, *mid-*, *dis-*, and *auto-*

Focus

- The prefix ***re-*** means "again."
- The prefix ***un-*** means "not" or "to do the opposite of."
- The prefix ***pre-*** means "before" or "ahead of."
- The prefix ***mis-*** means "wrong" or "bad."

Practice A **Add the given prefix to each word below. Write the new word and the meaning of the new word on the lines.**

	Prefix	Word	New Word	New Meaning
1.	*re-*	type	retype	to type again
2.	*mis-*	write	miswrite	to write something wrong
3.	*un-*	tie	untie	to do the opposite of tying
4.	*pre-*	chill	prechill	to chill something ahead of time
5.	*re-*	read	reread	to read again
6.	*pre-*	game	pregame	before the game
7.	*mis-*	shapen	misshapen	badly shaped
8.	*un-*	fold	unfold	to do the opposite of folding

Focus

- The prefix ***bi-*** means "two."
- The prefix ***mid-*** means "being the part in the middle." It begins many compound words.
- The prefix ***dis-*** means "not" or "to do the opposite of" something.
- The prefix ***auto-*** (sometimes spelled *aut-*) means "self" or "self-acting."

Practice B **Match each word with its meaning below.**

9. midweek
10. bicycle
11. disapprove
12. autopilot
13. disbelieve
14. bicolored
15. automatic
16. midnight

a. to not approve
b. something that happens on its own
c. a machine that has two wheels and pedals
d. the middle of the week
e. a machine that steers and pilots ships or spacecraft on its own
f. to not believe
g. the middle of the night
h. having two colors

Possible Answers: 9–d, 10–c, 11–a, 12–e, 13–f, 14–h, 15–b, 16–g

Write two sentences. In each sentence, use one of the above words that begins with *bi-*, *mid*, *dis-*, or *auto-*.

Possible Answers

17. I rode my bicycle today.
18. The pictures in this book are bicolored.

Name ______________________ Date __________

Affixes; Word Families; Multisyllabic Words with Silent Consonants

Focus

Prefixes and suffixes are types of **affixes.**

- An affix is its own syllable or syllables.

like (one syllable) ⟶ like • a • ble (three syllables)

- Affixes have their own meanings that change the meaning of the base word.

trust ⟶ *dis*trust ("to not trust")

Practice A

Divide each underlined word below into syllables. Then, circle the correct definition of the word.

1. The cranky girl was disagreeable.

   the state of not agreeing the state of agreeing

2. I got my favorite baseball player's autograph on my baseball.

   a person's name a person's self-written name

3. The group had an argument about who should go first.

   the process of arguing the process of not arguing

4. The beautiful sunset filled the sky with pinks and oranges.

   full of beauty able to have beauty

5. Janice will rewind the kite string on the spool.

   to do the opposite of winding to wind again

Lesson 5

Focus

A **word family** is a group of words that all have the same base word.

- When you add a prefix, suffix, *-ed,* or *-ing* to a base word, the words are in the same word family.
- Words in a word family can have different meanings. They can be different parts of speech.

Some words with many syllables have silent consonants. A **silent consonant** does not add a sound to a word. The letters *c, k,* and *gh* are sometimes silent.

Practice B

In the groups of words below, circle the two words that are in the same word family. Write the base word on the line.

6. readable reading watchable read
7. nicely unfriendly friendship friend
8. unharmed helpful harmful harm
9. arming disarm headed arm

Read each word below. Divide it into syllables. Circle it if it has a silent consonant.

10. scissors sci/ssors
11. clumping clum/ping
12. scenery sce/ner/y
13. knowing know/ing
14. darkly dark/ly
15. unscented un/scent/ed

Name ______________________ Date __________

Selection Vocabulary

deny (də • nī') *v.* to say that something is not true (page 328)

common (kom' • mən) *adj.* happening often; familiar (page 328)

shingle (shin' • gəl) *v.* to cover with shingles (page 329)

battered (bat' • tûrd) *v.* past tense of **batter:** to hit over and over again with heavy blows (page 330)

gust (gust) *n.* a sudden, strong rush of wind or air (page 332)

huddled (hud' • dəld) *v.* past tense of **huddle:** to crowd together (page 336)

haste (hāst) *n.* quickness in moving or in acting; speed (page 336)

calculate (kal' • kū • lāt') *n.* to figure out (page 336)

Practice **Write each vocabulary word next to the best example below.**

1. a blast of wind gust
2. having cereal for breakfast every day common
3. a group of people standing close together huddled
4. someone running to school haste
5. using an ax to chop at a tree over and over battered
6. working to put tiles on a roof shingle
7. working to figure out a math problem calculate
8. saying something is not true deny

Lesson 5

Apply **Write a vocabulary word to complete each rhyme below.**

9. The storm's winds will blow as they must,

   They pull at the house with each gust.

10. The noise makes my head feel all muddled,

    In the basement my cats are all huddled.

11. Outside trees sway as they're being battered

    By the rain, and now hail's being scattered.

12. But I'm happy, I cannot deny,

    Because inside I'm safe and I'm dry.

Use a vocabulary word to complete each sentence below.

13. In many parts of the country, thunderstorms are common and happen often.

14. Storms can move with great haste.

15. Meteorologists, or people who use science to predict the weather, work to calculate when storms will come.

16. But after a big storm, people may have to shingle their roofs again.

Name ______________________ Date __________

Compare and Contrast

Writers use **comparison** to make an idea clearer and to make a story more interesting to read.

- To **compare** means to tell how things, events, or characters are alike.
- To **contrast** means to tell how things, events, or characters are different.

Read each sentence below. Write *compare* if it compares two things. Write *contrast* if it contrasts. Write what two things are being compared or contrasted.

1. When I woke up yesterday, my head felt as heavy as stone.

compare; head and stone

2. The day was much darker than the day before.

contrast; the light one day and the light the day before

3. The clouds looked like angry faces in the sky.

compare; clouds and angry faces

4. Rain shot down on the house like arrows.

compare; rain and arrows

Lesson 5

Read each sentence from "McBroom and the Big Wind" below. Answer the questions.

The boys had left their marbles all over the field, and the marbles had grown as large as boulders.

5. Is the writer comparing or contrasting? comparing
What two things are being compared or contrasted?
the boys' marbles and boulders

Now that was a strong draft. But it wasn't a *big* wind. Nothing like the kind that broke my leg.

6. Is the writer comparing or contrasting? contrasting
What two things are being compared or contrasted?
the strong draft and the really big wind

So I made them wind shoes—made 'em out of heavy iron skillets. Out in the breeze those shoes felt light as feathers.

7. Is the writer comparing or contrasting? comparing
What two things are being compared or contrasted?
the weight of the shoes and the weight of feathers

Lesson 5

Writing a Mystery

Audience: Who will read your mystery?

Possible Answer my classmates

Purpose: What is your reason for writing the mystery?

Possible Answer I want to make up a story about a creepy house I saw.

Prewriting **Use this graphic organizer to take notes for your mystery.**

Possible Answers **Story Map**

Beginning

Hailey and Nate notice strange noises coming from the old house.

↓

Middle

They try to figure out what's going on. They decide the house is haunted.

↓

End

It turns out that a stray cat is living in the house.

Revising

Use this checklist to revise your mystery.

- ☐ Does your mystery have a clear problem to be solved?
- ☐ Do you use details to give a clear picture of characters and setting?
- ☐ Do your clues lead to the solution?
- ☐ Does your ending make sense?
- ☐ Did you use words that add to the suspense and surprise in the story?

Editing/Proofreading

Use this checklist to correct mistakes.

- ☐ Did you indent your paragraphs?
- ☐ Did you use correct spelling?
- ☐ Did you use quotation marks around dialogue?
- ☐ Did you capitalize proper nouns and the first words of sentences?
- ☐ Did you use correct punctuation?

Publishing

Use this checklist to prepare your mystery for publication.

- ☐ Neatly rewrite or type a final copy.
- ☐ Add a drawing.

Name ____________________ Date __________

Spelling

Focus The spelling words in this lesson review the prefixes *re-, un-, pre-, mis-, bi-, mid-,* and *dis-,* word families, words with /n/, /r/, and /j/ sound spellings, and affixes that change word meaning.

Practice **Sort the spelling words under the correct heading.**

Order will vary under heading.

Part of the word family *final*

1. final
2. finish
3. finite

Affixes that change meaning

4. homeless
5. beautiful
6. rewrite
7. unwrap
8. precook
9. mistreat
10. midnight
11. dislike

Word List

1. wreck
2. rewrite
3. unwrap
4. final
5. finish
6. finite
7. knack
8. precook
9. mistreat
10. biceps
11. midnight
12. dislike
13. judge
14. homeless
15. beautiful

Challenge Words

16. scenery
17. nonfiction
18. huddled

Spelling (continued)

Prefixes *re-, un-, pre-, mis-, bi-, mid-,* and *dis-*

12. rewrite
13. unwrap
14. precook
15. mistreat
16. biceps
17. midnight
18. dislike

/n/, /r/, /j/ sound/spellings

19. wreck
20. final
21. knack
22. finish
23. judge
24. finite
25. unwrap
26. midnight
27. rewrite
28. unwrap
29. precook
30. mistreat

Name ______________________ Date __________

Adverbs; Synonyms and Antonyms: Subject/Verb Agreement; Verb Tenses

An **adverb** tells more about a verb, an adjective, or another adverb.

Many adverbs end in *-ly.*

When describing a good action, make sure to use the adverb *well.*

Adverbs can tell *how* something is done, *where* something happens, *when* or *for how long* something happens, or *how certain* we are about something that happens.

Synonyms are words with the same or nearly the same meaning.

Antonyms are words with opposite meanings.

Practice A

Read the following sentence. Then, answer the questions below.

The wind skipped quickly across the prairie today.

1. What are the two adverbs in this sentence? quickly, today
2. Which adverb tells more about how something was done? quickly
3. Which adverb tells more about when something was done? today
4. Give a synonym for *quickly.* **Possible Answer** speedily
5. Give an antonym for *quickly.* **Possible Answer** slowly

Focus

- If the subject is singular, the present tense form of the verb usually ends in *-s* or *-es.*
- If the subject is plural, do not add anything to the verb to form the present tense.
- Many verbs form the past tense by adding *-d* or *-ed* to the present tense form.
- The future tense is formed by using the helping verb *will.*
- Some verbs are irregular; they do not follow the rules.

Practice B **Choose the correct verb for each sentence and write it on the line.**

1. Roshawna ___is___ a storyteller. (are/is)

2. She and her sister ___tell___ stories together. (tells/tell)

3. Last week, they ___went___ to a story festival. (went/goed)

4. Roshawna ___had___ a lot of fun. (have/had)

5. Next month they ___will go___ on a trip to Africa. (will go/went)

6. They ___will study___ with a South African storyteller there. (will studies/will study)

7. Roshawna ___is___ excited. (is/was)

8. She ___has packed___ her bag already! (has packed/have packed)

Name ______________________ Date __________

Comparing Information Across Sources

Good writers use the most reliable sources available. To make sure that information is correct, cross-checking between sources is sometimes necessary.

To make sure that your sources are reliable, consider the following points:

- Is the source written by an expert? Book jackets and notes at the beginning or end of articles sometimes give information about the authors.
- Is the source up-to-date? Would another source be more up-to-date?
- Is the information detailed enough?
- Is the information relevant to the topic?

Sources you might have used:

Encyclopedias	Books	Magazines
Newspapers	Videos	Interviews
Personal Experiences	Museums	Internet

Think about your unit investigation. On the lines below, list the sources that you are using. Then, write what other sources you can use to check the information that you received from the original sources.

Possible Answers

Sources used: World Book Encyclopedia

Sources to check against: another encyclopedia

Sources used: a book of different Cinderella stories

Sources to check against: a Web site that tells about Cinderella stories

Sources used: a video showing how to tell stories

Sources to check against: a book about storytelling

Sources used: my memory of seeing story quilts at the library

Sources to check against: a Web site about story quilts

Sources used: a Web site about petroglyphs

Sources to check against: an encyclopedia article about petroglyphs

Name ______________________________ Date ____________

Proofreading Marks

Mark	Meaning	Example
¶	Indent	¶ Once upon a time, many years ago, there lived a dinosaur named Rocky. He lived . . .
^	Add something.	a ^shiny penny
̸	Take out something.	Rabbits live in in burrows.
≡	Make a capital letter.	california
/	Make a small letter.	We go camping in Summer.
sp ◯	Check spelling.	sp (freind)
⊙	Add a period.	There are eight planets in the solar system ⊙